good deed rain

Follow Your Friend © 2023
Allen Frost, Good Deed Rain
Bellingham, Washington
ISBN: 979-8-8689-0974-0

Writing 1989—2023: Allen Frost
Cover Illustration: Rosa Frost
Cover Production: Priya Shalauta

Credits:
p.53 by Aaron Gunderson from *Pie in the Sky #93*
p.111 train by Michael Paulus
p.126 A. Gunderson cover for *The End of Beryllium*
p.146 A. Gunderson from *Pie in the Sky #10*
p.184 cover by Rustle Frost
p.206 cover by Rosa Frost
p.274 cover by Rosa Frost
p.279 cover by Michael Paulus
p.290 page from *Pie in the Sky #84*
Other pictures and covers by author
Apple: TFK!

Quote:
Nathaniel Hawthorne, *The American Notebooks*, Ohio
State University Press, 1932.

FOLLOW YOUR FRIEND

Allen Frost

Good Deed Rain ◊ Bellingham, Washington ◊ 2023

"A person to catch fireflies, and try to kindle his household fire with them. It would be symbolical of something."

—Nathaniel Hawthorne

LAWN VETERANS

For a while now I've wondered about gathering the animals from my writing into an animal book. This summer I finally began that roundup. There are a lot of them! They're hiding in novels, poetry, essays, and short stories. I couldn't catch them all, but here are some favorites. Mostly there are animals from around our neighborhood: birds, rabbits, deer, owls, and coyotes. There are also elephants, lions, dinosaurs, unicorns and the like (and I'm not sure if mermaids count but they're here too). This isn't a zoo with the occupants put in order by continents, it ordered itself while I went through stacks of Good Deed Rain. Before I printed books in the format you hold, I used to make cardstock handsewn books or stapled *Pie in the Sky*. Photocopy was the printing press of the day. From 1989—2012, from *Lawn Veterans* to *The Peaceful Island*.

the
peaceful
island

You'll find migrations across these pages. Animals helped with my own migrations too, from Seattle, to Portland, to Ohio, and back to the Northwest. There's a reason you find them on totem poles, invisibly guiding or otherwise.

Finally, in order to keep this from becoming "The Best of the Animals," the book ends with the release of a new collection of animal stories, *Octopus Motors*.

I hope you find more friends waiting for you just ahead.

—A.F, Sept 8 '23

WHERE THEY COME FROM:

Something Bright (2021)
Homeless Sutra (2018)
Pie in the Sky (1993-94)
Poems in Zoos (1990)
Water Everywhere (1990)
Paying for Water (1990)
Lawn Veterans (1989)
The Yellow Day (1993)
How to Build a Birdhouse Out of Love Poems (1993)
King Leopold's Slow Leak (2000)
Almost Animals (2018)
Fable (2018)
Violet of the Silent Movies (2020)
The Peaceful Island (2012)
Thriftstore Madonna (2021)
Forest & Field (2022)
Snow White Moth (2008)
A Parents' Guide to Raising Piranha (2004)
Sinking Celestial (2006)
In the Summer Air (2005)
The New Book of Endangered Birds (2004)
Last Ohio Morning (2004)
The End of Beryllium (1997)
Sacred Heart Junkyard (2006)
The 500 Pound Halo (2002)
Paper Cup (2002)
Your Favorite World (1998)

The Charts of the Sea (2006)
Magic Island (2022)
Not to Worry (2011)
Travel (2012)
The Wonderful Stupid Man (2012)
Wave #1-#3 (1997)
14 Animals (2012)
Signals (2011)
The Yellow Tree (2010)
Animals, Ghosts & Outer Space (2010)
The Welfare Office (2019)
Red Leaf Boat (2022)
Royalty Toy Company (1999)
Up #2 (1994)
Ohio Time (2007)
Trelawny Cable Car (2003)
A Reversed Cat (2010)
Octopus Motors (2023)

Also appearing in: *Bowl of Water* (2004), *Another Life* (2007), *Home Recordings* (2009), *Playground* (2014), *The Sylvan Moore Show* (2015), *Imaginary Someone* (2020)

The BIRD BOOK MIGRATION

Every year at this time, the bird book hops to the edge of the shelf, opens its cover wings and flaps around the room wildly. It stirs the curtains as it bumps against the window. The gray sky is beckoning. I hold the book carefully and bring it to the door. I know I won't see it for a while. Way past the telephone wires, up above town, a formation circles.

A RARE SIGHT on a WINTER DAY

Three butterflies gather around a cigarette someone left on the sidewalk. It's cold enough they need to wear their winter coats, scarves and hats. They hold their hands to the heat and stamp their feet and one of them says something, a word that makes a cloud so miniscule you need a microscope to see.

The ORANGE HORSE

Once upon a time there was an orange horse in a field in Scotland. I remember its name was Fred. That's what the American called it. He wore cowboy boots. He came from Texas to work on the oil rigs. Whenever he wasn't at sea, he would go to the fence and hang his arms out and the horse would run to him from wherever it happened to be.

APPARENTLY a BIRD

Apparently there's a bird that causes insomnia. It likes to perch by a window early before dawn and it takes every stress, regret, undone worry, every woe that could possibly toss and stretch your conscience, each wish and wrong bend in memory, and it turns them into song. Sometimes it will sing for hours. You can't help but listen. The pharmacy sells a remedy. It comes in a little paper box to put on your sill. I don't know if it works.

ASLEEP in OHIO

A baby stroller ride away from our Ohio rental house, down the clacking cement path by the road, onto Ontario, we would sing and talk and point out birds in yards. At Meeker Street we were close to sleep. It idled in the transformers, lay in the grass surrounding the power substation hum. That's where we stopped and counted rabbits. We made up names for them and gave them jobs they liked to do (tuning circuits, adjusting wires, checking levels and turning dials). We imagined their homes and families underground, where bunnies had their dinners, blew out candles and went to bed. Sure enough, one more yawn and we could turn around.

HER LITTLE FARM

In her apartment she has a goat, a chicken, and a talking crow. Oh, and a beehive by the window. Corn grows in flowerpots. At night, she can hear the barn owl behind the wall, hunting in the vast dark distance between the standing lamp and the kitchenette.

A BITE of APPLE

A few weeks have gone since our dog died and I still go to the backyard to check on her, see that the snow is a blanket, and the blackberries are standing guard. She doesn't follow me back to the house, but every time I cut an apple, I think how she would be waiting for a bite.

BETTY'S DOG

Betty's dog stands by the door and wags her tail. Her eyes are like marbles. She doesn't need them to know we're there. She leans a little against the other dog as they move backwards to let us inside. 1975 was her house in Massachusetts and the people came and went, and dreams and days were all the same, seen without sight.

A BLUE OCTOPUS

On another planet or a cartoon universe, they have a streetsweeper too. You hear the rumble for half a block as it nears. The birds of the neighborhood flee in front. Next door it sounds like a three-headed dog is warning us. Then it appears. A steam-driven wheelbarrow, steered by a blue octopus, clearing the pavement with a dustpan and broom.

The FRIENDLY GIANT

The Friendly Giant had a castle I went to every morning when I was one. The music would play, he would let down the drawbridge and open the doors. An imaginary world as unreal as California seems to me now, animals, songs, something to laugh about, until it was time to say goodbye. Then the doors and the drawbridge would close, and the castle would turn into sky. I was only beginning to see every day starting and ending the same way.

The SEA VISITOR, part 1

The tide is low, showing the flats and mats of seaweed that carpet the underwater floor. When the sea is gone it leaves all its clutter everywhere. I like to see what I can find. Shells and bits of colored glass fill my hand. I go past them with wet shoes to where the last big rock is parked, sunk like a Pontiac. I stand on the dented, barnacle roof and look over the edge into the deep emerald-green start of the Pacific Ocean.

The SEA VISITOR, part 2

I think a submarine could come pop up right beside me and I wouldn't mind. I would wait for the crew to unscrew the hatch and I might go with them on some adventure under icebergs and sunsets to a jungle island full of dinosaurs. Amazing places I can only visit with crayons. Or maybe this rock itself will let me climb inside and I can look out windows like someone in the backseat of a car watching a rainy day.

The SEA VISITOR, part 3

That's when I see somebody else in my reflection below. Two eyes set in a gray ghost-like blur. A couple bubbles lift it closer to the surface and then a seal appears, close enough for me to reach and pet. I think of feeding it (we have some fish at home) and caring for it, being its friend, and I can put it in a wagon and bring it to school, or the swimming pool. I'm so excited thinking about the things we will do together, I don't have time to say goodbye.

A BETTER, MORE PEACEFUL WORLD

A large moth knocked on the door today. I could see his antennas and fedora through the little window, but I opened the door anyway. What the hell. Let me tell you, there's no way to prepare yourself for the sight of a 6-foot moth in a brown suit trying to hand you a brochure about a better, more peaceful world.

CRABGRASS

I took our puppy for a walk in the woods. She was sniffing the air, standing on her back legs, pulling on the leash like a fairground ride, sure something was ahead of us. I know what it is: Spring. When I let her go in the field, she took off after that ball of bright light. It was warm as a sun, bouncing up the path with her running after. Every time it touched the ground, it left a green splash in the crabgrass.

The RABBIT TELEGRAPH

I wrote most of *Simple-Minded Sunshine* in the early morning, in the half hour or so I had before I left for work. It was a long gray winter and I was thinking of those mysterious rabbit characters: Uncle Wiggly, Br'er Rabbit, Harvey. Spring brings sunshine and rabbits and deer start to appear. We see them in the woods when I walk the dog, but I also noticed we had a visitor sitting in our yard while I wrote. Near the last page of this book, I looked out the window and saw a rabbit at our doorstep, intent as a telegraph operator sending out messages. I think that probably explains where this story comes from.

JACK SHELLAC'S ART SHACK

The cameras were rolling, filming as he lay the thick color paint across the canvas. He had a running dialogue going, something about how beautiful camping in the Appalachians is...The leaves, the swaying trees and purple lakes, the haunting call of the loon...He made a joke about not paying the trailer park, leaving in his Winnebago early before the ranger woke up. While he began adding a deer to the rippling edge of the water, there was a crash and a boom-mic swung wildly. Jack's banter ceased abruptly, his ashen face staring in horror at the approaching sight—an eight-foot bear, walking on it hind legs, panting, slobbering and slashing its claws and teeth. It fell over Jack like a shadow and the scenic painting stuck to its hair while the TV crew retreated, leaving the cameras fixed on the grizzly.

AT NIGHT

Out along the road, where
there were wolves long ago
they would hang out
and drink beer on the big rock
spraypainted with heavy metal
band names and girlfriends
since become wives.
At night
the sounds of cars
passing with headlights
glowing in the dark woods
they would blow into bottles
and sound like wolves.

HANK WILLIAMS' DOG

Hank Williams had a dog he brought with him touring the small towns, the lost highways to the bars and cheap halls of America forty years ago. Hank Williams' Dog lived the life of Hank Williams: getting into fights in alleys, getting drunk and stumbling across the country to perform. On a hot night in Tennessee, the dog outdrank his passed-out owner and veered through the door, off the porch, tripped, down the gulley, unconscious, and into the open arms of a cold river current running to the sea.

MEXICAN DOG BISCUITS

The car was parked out in the dust, as clouds bunched together over the brown mountains and began to move slowly. Inside the house, the American tourist was busy cutting hair for the entire Gonzalez family. They were lined up oldest to youngest and he moved with his scissors from the white thin hair of the grandfather, along towards the black braids of the little girl at the end, holding in her arms a sleeping baby.

It began to rain while he cut and showered the floor with their hair. He had never been in a rain like this before. The tin roof shook and bounced and the lights dimmed from the water eclipse. The children shrieked and leaped out of the line to run outside and splash. They let a river in every time the door opened and closed. They settled down when the weather passed and when they came back in, the American trimmed their wet hair.

That's what he did in the U.S, he told them. He had his own barber shop in Seattle where it always rained, but not like how it does here. He made a rain sound and drummed his fingers on the top of his head and everyone laughed. Then he opened the door to go to his car.

He stared and dropped his black bag. His convertible was filled with water. It looked like a swimming pool on wheels.

Still, he made it back to Seattle. The car was a submarine, it was sluggish and it agonized on the mountains up through California, but at last, he made it home. His dog was glad to see him return and jumped all over him. The clothes and luggage were all damp in the trunk and he threw them straight into the washing machine. There was also a cardboard box filled with soggy dog biscuits— treats for his dog—souvenirs. He laid them out like tiles to dry on the kitchen counters and across a table in the sunlight.

The MUSIC of HER CLOCK

He needed to open the window a bit, it was so hot. She could only sleep in tropical heat, all night long the iron grill at the foot of their bed would blow. At five o'clock the music of her clock would wake her and slowly she would roll away from him to the shower, while he slept on.

Irene had left for work already, by now she was at the café serving early breakfast.

Ray peeled off the sheet and stuck his legs out onto the black carpet. The only light in the room came from the red digital clock glow. The dark windows rattled a storm blowing up off the lake. Out there, waves would be crashing all over the shore. Ray reached past the curtain and lifted the window, cold air rushed inside. The rose tree scratched against the glass.

He crawled back under the covers, lying over the warm shape left on her side of the bed. He fell asleep again.

A window shutter banging woke him up.

The room, a shade of blue, was very cold. A few leaves had blown inside. Silhouettes of furniture, the purple dresser and the bookshelf against the wall. At least an hour must have passed since he opened the window. He had a thought of Irene serving eggs to people as he dragged himself to the window and shut it.

When he was back in bed he heard the purr from the corner. A cat had curled herself there on the tangle of clothes. She must have come in out of the storm, Ray wondered, rolled over, and went back to sleep.

The cat turned in his dream and became a tall metal bridge he was walking on. Underneath, riverwater rolled, carrying houses, cars, parking lots, stores, an entire slow town drifting past. Then his alarm clock bell went off and he reached out of the dream to hit it off.

Irene had her clock to go to work by and Ray had his. Ray yawned, stretched away. The room was warm again at eight o'clock. Already he had forgotten his dream, but there opposite him was the cat. Sometime since her arrival through the cold window, he could hear the small noises, there was now a kitten. Ray came closer to her and saw the one white pearl against her side.

LOVELY RITA

The moment the duckling's beak broke through the hard shell and the small eyes opened to the world, there was Rodney. This was the moment Rodney had been waiting for, riding his bicycle home from school, fast, to watch the egg, to hold the brown egg in his cupped hands, wishing it to open. When the egg became the yellow bird, it was a large miracle and he named her Rita. Rodney became all she needed; she saw nothing strange in the tall giant shape of him. She would follow everywhere in his eight-foot shadow, as they walked together on the sidewalk to grade school, running to keep up with him if he jumped a fence. He understood her language when she quacked, if she meant food or rest or a swim in the stream. After a whole day together, until the sun rested,she would sleep close beside him at night, curled. Rita didn't make a sound as he rolled over in the dark in his sleep and smothered her. The giant woke up in the morning and she was snapped. He couldn't stop his tears across the ground he fell upon. The howling giant built a tower for her out of broken cement, dirt and tree limbs, colored pieces of metal and glass. Soon he could look down on skyscrapers from his grief with jets and rockets around him. Still, he built higher. Clouds and the weather formed around him, up and up, taller through the atmosphere. He took fiery comets, also stars and he kept building, adding planets and the solar system, galaxies and finally the universe itself.

JIM CHAMPAGNE

The woman on the payphone
kept asking for Jim Champagne.
I overheard her as I walked past.
Jim Champagne, that rings a bell,
but I couldn't remember why.
"Well, where is he?"
her shouting faded,
"I have to talk to him!
It's important!"
Apparently he wasn't there.
I thought about him,
where did I hear that name?
Suddenly it occurred to me
I could see him in a choppy sea
maybe the Adriatic
he's trading military secrets
for fish.
Jim Champagne was a trained spy seal.
On his nose he wore radar
and carried plans and real-estate
rolled in a waterproof tube.
But Jim Champagne was in trouble
she was calling him to warn him
"The Coast Guard knows everything!

The oysters were bugged in that café!"
Jim got the picture loud and clear.
He was splashing, swimming
against undertow and Gulf Stream
with all the forces of America
after him.

SALMON AVENUE

Through the steam
and water of my shower
salmon are moving
upstream.
Somehow they've taken
the industrial route
into pipes under sidewalks
and sprinklers on lawns.
When oceans, rivers,
and lakes are the past,
chopped up and polluted
memories,
they find
their water
elsewhere,
swimming past
my feet on their way
to a full bathtub
or a reservoir.

PETS

Now with science we can make our own animals, from the circus or a zoo at a size convenient for you. Elephants are popular, shrunk down to 20 inches tall, holding to your leg as you move from room to room A small blue whale in a goldfish bowl, spouting every half hour like a cuckoo-clock to keep time by. An ostrich in a canary's wooden cage, flapping its wings in the sunlight coming through the window. A hippo curling in your arms and purring like a cat when its stomach is rubbed. With all the animal kingdom to pick from, his possibilities were exciting and pet stores took on a magical glow like the colors and chrome of a dreamed 1956 Chevrolet showroom. He would carry home a four-inch buffalo scratching in a little paper box. There were airholes poked in the top and as he walked he could inspect to see his pet move. And he would let his buffalo loose on the gold carpet of his bedroom floor, watching it roam the prairie floor, past the toy model railroad stretching from one corner to the other like Manifest Destiny miniaturized.

WILLIAM CARLOS WILLIAMS for BEGINNERS

She was a sad woman with a Stan Laurel look. In the morning on the subway to work, she sat among people like they were made of glass, pushed around her the same as windows.

She had just come to the United States, to share that American dream that passed around cooking fires at night. Like the church promises of Heaven, if she prayed, she would get there.

But when she slept, she dreamed back through the city to Guatemala, to the greens and warms and villages connected by dirt roads and barking dogs. In her sleep she remembered it all, as if she was still there. Then she would wake up to more gunshots and sirens, but the voices would remind her where she was—in a country where she was learning from a book how to speak.

She was in America alone with William Carlos Williams who made words on the page to look up at her in quiet short rows. She would break them off like flowers and look for their meaning in her Spanish dictionary, learning to speak again. That first week in America when she applied for a job as a cleaning lady in a midtown hotel, she recited "The Red Wheelbarrow," pushing the words slowly before her.

HER COMFORT DISAPPEARED in GREEN SMOKE

There was an artificial leg hanging in the window
there used to be electricity for Christmas lights
until everyone ran out of money for utilities
and then it was down to survival of the fittest.
The oven door stayed open and poured out heat
someone slept in front of the 400 degrees.
It was winter, we were reduced to candles.
Construction sights supplied plywood for fires
and Misty the dog watched us burn her couch.
Her comfort disappeared in green smoke
except for a cushion she got to keep in the
corner.

WALLS COULD BE WALKED THROUGH

I found The Professor in the parking lot one late night. Someone had abandoned him there. I picture a shady car escaping along the dark lake. I brought the kitten inside, he was frozen in shock. He wasn't afraid of water though. I washed him in the sink and it warmed him and then he fell asleep inside my shirt next to me.

The Professor returned slowly, day by day. I gave him the content life of a cat and he started to remember life and be interested in what surrounded him. But he couldn't live with me the way I was living at that time. I was a one-man nightmare of ghosts and things and flying machines.

So my friend took the lucky cat with him to a house in Ocean Shores. The cat could roam in fields next to the Pacific and when the sun went down, he could find home at night. One time a bat circled the living room in swooping blind turns, brushing the walls until its radar clicked on the open screen door. There were birds and mice, dogs, horses, loud tourists, motor scooters, and owls in the black tree canopy.

Soon my friend started to notice the unusual things about the cat. Walls could be walked through, invisibility, anti-gravity leaps through the branches, the power to control where it wanted to be.

When my friend ran into money trouble—his books weren't selling—he lost the lease on the house, and he had to return to the city. Of course, the cat hated being back in the city and one day he was let outside and he didn't come back.

We imagined him walking beside the highway and dusty county roads in rain, over bridges, finally returning to the ocean he loved.

WORM FARM

It's not hard to see why the economy is crumbled, see how they cut down all the trees and left the hills brown. Make the best of a broken situation, work in the city, save as much as you can, though it won't be easy living here. But think of the land. After all the pavement and cement of this place, wait and keep that moment in sight, when all your money from five dollar an hour jobs will become your beautiful farm by the ocean.

DREAM with MEXICANS and FLOATING LIONS

In big wooden cages, the lions floated ashore. They broke out of the surf onto the sand, angry and looking for food. Their roars carried all the way from the sea up to the town. We turned from the cliff where we were watching. I held her hand tightly and we ran to look for shelter. The houses were all locked and boarded up except for one and we hurried towards the open door. Maybe we could hide down in the basement where the lions could scratch but couldn't get in? We ran up the path, almost safe, when suddenly a Mexican family pushing a piano and moving boxes and furniture blocked the doorway. They couldn't understand our warnings, our hysterical shouting and pointing at the ocean.

POSIE CRUTCHFIELD in:
EVERY KIND of ANIMAL

Once again, Posie Crutchfield didn't have the ten dollars for rent, once again she had to pack her cardboard suitcase and walk out in the black with her umbrella, back onto the street. She thought maybe her luck would change in another city. She turned towards the railyard, its loud smoke of trains leaving every hour. The smoke wasn't only from steam engines pulling in and out of the station, Posie dropped her bag and umbrella to run into the shipwrecked ark. It looked like it fell out of the air. One by one, she freed every kind of animal. She brought out cats and dogs, let the birds fly, and she escaped with fish cupped in her hands. Two goats, llamas, Clydesdale horses, three cows, a gorilla pair, anteaters and lions. Finally, with the last mouse on her arm, she collapsed in the grass. She dreamed she was Noah, in a flowing robe, with a staff, drifting, watching for land on the endless ocean horizon. All the animals, two of each kind, were watching her watch the water. She never got to finish the dream, she woke in a rolling boxcar, surrounded by the pets who followed her.

NORTH 48th STREET

After another day
climbing green trees
playing through yards
and down alleys
games that claim
the whole neighborhood
as the world
sitting on the steps
and listening

I'm remembering

As the sun sets
if the wind is right
on those summer nights
I can hear the zoo
transmitted on the air
like radio

A lion roars
calling out
from his throne
in a cage
diminishing in waves
like a stone
skipped across
the rooftops

the yellow tree

allen frost

The YELLOW DAY

It opens up like a box of sun
with birds and a rusting tractor
anchored asleep in the weeds
We walked along the farm path
beside the parched riverbed
and I named the snake
that broke in front of us

SAMMY SLITHER

There he goes
through the dry grass
between two rivers
and a bridge and
he isn't taking his time
he goes as fast as possible

HERE is the WINGTRIPPLE YOU THOUGHT YOU THREW to the GLOOM

He gave the Wingtripple away so many times it now lay in tatters. Barely a light breathed in it anymore. When he put it on the windowsill at night, the moths weren't even attracted. So he crumpled it up and let go. It skidded and shuddered through the window, falling to the cement, squashed on the sidewalk below. It didn't matter that he was empty inside. A day passed without a Wingtripple, a week, or was it a year? Yes, it must have been a year, it was winter again and he walked watching his feet. Cold holes in his soles, cracked paving, it didn't matter to him that time had become heavy as concrete. Scuffing shoes, traffic, a jet, a siren. Then the noise of a different thing pried like a dream off the beak of a flower and landed on him. Sometimes a Wingtripple disappears, but it always comes back.

The OSTRICH LISTENING to the WIND CALL HER NAME for the FIRST TIME

Separating herself from the cattails proved to be more difficult than she thought. Not only had she made a home for herself in their raking clack, she could remain perfectly hidden as long as she wanted. If the wind hadn't called her name so warmly, she might never have left. Like a ballerina putting on rainy day galoshes, her leg umbrellaed from the weeds to extend onto the flurried swinging reflections of a caterpillar world.

YOU ARE

you are

the nursery rhyme
of the tides

the jumping sound
of cricket wires

the spelling bees
in flowers

the sun
in the eyes
of a rabbit

BIRDS WATCHED the ANGELS to LEARN to FLY

You think the world is a glowing thing
You think of yourself as a bird flown here
You let yourself sing on the wires
That cross and tangle up the city
Sometimes though
You forget to be what you are
You listen to their sound instead
Their rusty creak of radio noise
And you feel what they must feel
Paralyzed in a gray day to day
In times like these
You have to get off the ground
Put yourself back in the wings of a tree
Dry off the rain of your tears
And make music clear as poetry

BARNS

There's nothing like finding yourself
lost in fog and a spinning clock
on a road serenaded by cows
in a hundred clouds
in shoals of barns
all alike in the night

COW

I live in green
I eat flowers
I stand around
watching the clouds
or watching the ground

OTHER PATCHES of the SKY

She lay on her back, to point at the sky.
Through the lens, all the clouds in the blue
paddled by, while she waited for the moment
to arrive. When a bird flew across the glass,
she would capture it in a photograph.
She would take it home inside the camera
and in the red lights of the dark room,
release it again to the world.
Swirled in the water and chemicals,
the bird would reemerge slowly.
Dripping, becoming real, then pinned
to dry on a singing rope with other
patches of the sky.

SINGING FILLED LEAVES

I can't keep
these birds
in here

the sound
spills out
like silver
from a yellow
bucket

and singing
fills the leaves

IMAGINE THE THINGS I WILL SEE AND KNOW

Moth listened to their buzzing words of advice, warnings curled with fluttering and circles cutting circles, made to emphasize the dangers out there.

Moth heard through all their doom but told them again that he was leaving this home. "I have to see more at night than a distant moon." He had heard tales of electricity that poured itself in rivers down streets and filled up all the many eyes of skyscrapers…So beautiful you couldn't look away. "Imagine the things I will see and know," moth said.

His wings held wide to say goodbye. Then off he flew, sailing by constellations for the brightest dot of distant city light.

In this NIGHT of GRASSHOPPER SWINGING STARS

There is a gentleness in this night of grasshopper swinging stars. Green drops of pearly light. Fly lullabies where they hide folded under the eaves of the sleeping house. Moths tired too, with their laundry-white wings hung on the windowpanes of his room. Like two or three hedgehogs lumped on soft, he watches out of the cave in the covers and instead of the Moon, which he sees every eve, that round shapes into something he can hardly believe. Blink, he dazzles, looks again to make sure, but there's no doubt and what's more, now there is sound. A melody all nature responds to. He would sit up in bed, but he's almost too amazed, as he stares from flannel and sheets. Moon's happy disguise, a gold record in the sky, plays fiddle as song down to blue Earth, down to the wide drifting heather and meadow where a cow lifts her head up to fly.

The UNDERWATER WORLD

The pond has gone and with it the fish and the fences. Missing water, my field has a dark scoop in the ground. It looks as if big hands have come down from the sky, cupped and taken away what I loved so much. Something that was supposed to last forever and always has disappeared with a simple wind, I guess.

Every day for the longest dream, I put on the golden diving suit, left from the house with hurried footsteps through the wild grass and flowers to step deep into the pond. Bubbles popped around me. I had fences made of waterlily so the small fish could grow safely into bigger fish. That was all important at the time, to repair green plants and make sure everything swam fine. I brought food too, it felt so good to be in the underwater world. So what did I do wrong to lose it all? I really don't even know. I haven't learned a thing. Watching the clouds, I just continue to pray that it will rain again, to fill with water what is gone.

EYES AWAKE

Frog listens to the rain with his eyes awake, night hangs from the leaves, life is spoken by a million drops of water. They talk of journeys by cloud, dreaming and falling, knowing and not forgetting, singing on the way down, only heard when they land.

The AIR BESIDE ME

I live on a leaf, I've gone all the way out
to the end of the wind, holding on where
silkworms lay down silver threads
Green branches rub and saw like violins
and birds tip their wings on the air beside me
Sunlight breeze and stars at night
the hush of thoughts in my head
This is the faraway world I find myself in
where I may never have to worry
because I believe in the leaves

BIRDCOAT

When you need air
to get up and away
from crooked ground
and all that's wrong
put on the birdcoat

Its colored feathers
are woven in yarns
wings for arms

The roofs like bottlecaps below
while crows and even clouds
will swim out of your path

pie in the sky

number eighty four

YOU in the FALLING RAIN and
EVERYTHING

Finding you in this quiet place
the calm trees of the glade, waterlilies
stepped on the pond with green fingerprints
the call of birds like music on the radio

Not all of America has been uprooted
It takes patience and exploring through
the backstreets, past tangled barbed wire
over the bottled caught up talk in circles
out to where I can think straight and see
you in the falling rain and everything

GUARANTEE

Out of the tumbled driftwood, they have built themselves a house. Slung like carp, its wooden lines fishtailed with seaweed, dried, and brine, so close to the ocean, up from sand, hightide waves masquerading as lawn. On a stormy night, they are guaranteed starfish visitors.

DEWIE the DORMOUSE and TOAD RICKY

The sunny lemonade of the hot day fried on the road. Toad Ricky was riding his bicycle, his long green legs bending with the pedal spins that took him further and further away from home. The song in the air was a bluebird following him with bounces from post to post. Heat bugs chimed the degrees, and a butterfly fanned its yellow wings on the handlebars. Toad Ricky was happy to be sailing on this tar river between green shady trees that gradually shrank into the twigs and dusty weeds of the desert.

"Brrr..." he shivered finally. The sun was going down behind mountain shapes. It glinted its last orange goodbye on the railroad tracks that seemed to string forever like silver shadows under the telephone wires.

Down the road, miles away, Dewie the Dormouse, sitting on a telephone book, pressed a foot on the extended pedal. The truck went faster. The headlights flared their yellow sight into the black night and Dewie pulled the horn cord so its mournful voice carried like a moose searching for love in the sage and tumbleweeds with darkness everywhere.

But not without life, there were coyote slinking around the road, badgers tending a fire, an owl clutching hotel keys in flight, and just like another big midnight animal, the truck slowed down, and stopped in the sand to let the skinny toad and his bicycle hop on board.

TOAD RICKY RETURNS for a WATERFALL

Toad's legs turned bicycle wheels. For a long time they spun miles. First the sun then the moon sailed overhead. Green eyes, star guided, riding towards dawn. Morning bird songs filled the sky. The dew on the hills made silver oceans. Flowers schooled like fish waking up. Around the corner the road folded and cupped a puddle in the middle. Toad's eyes glimmered, the thought of riding straight through the splash, putting water into the air, and to maybe hang a rainbow there. So he sped up his pedaling and got low over the handlebars. A couple rabbits saw it happen—the bicycle submerged in a wave and Toad Ricky was gone.

NEW LIFE

I borrowed five elephants and took them through Seattle to where the wall of death trolled itself under the bridge. They toppled it over and turned it to dust, then we built a fifty-foot cabbage that glows peacefully at night.

MIGRATING BIRDS

Over the rained-on field
littered with pumpkins
broken like pottery

The OLD GOAT

On the way to the bus each dawn I walked through a field on a path dug in bracken and thorn. I waited for the appearance of the mythical beast in leaves and sure enough he would be there, torn above the old glass gourds of wine, inside a window full of vines. A long white beard and curling over horns and eyes like blue marbles sunk so deep in the dew.

The COW on the MOON

The Cow on the Moon sings songs of
loneliness with her warm harp-woven moo.
She's jumped this far and she's forgotten
how to get back.

EMILY DICKINSON

I mistook the shadow
of a flower
for a spider
so dark
against the ground
its petals
made legs of blue

The $50 RABBIT

Who would have known what we paid
to get where we are, that desperate
on the other side of this counter
we signed over traveler checks
and he gave us a toy-prize rabbit
for a list of houses and apartments
we might rent out

The OCELOT

When he rented another apartment, he told the landlord he had "a kitty." It was in the cage he carried, quiet and sleek and its spots had a lulling hypnotic power. The truth wasn't revealed until the cat hopped off the radiator and escaped through the open window. The sight of it caught in flashlights on the stair railing drove all the tenants outside at midnight. They stared like moths from the ragged lawn. That was the end of its stay there. To its way of thinking, the jungle was forever gone, its home of walls was always shifting, there was something wrong with the world.

HAP

Hap parked his car
in the garden by the road

The blue jays parted
on his way down

WILMA

The wooded hill behind the warehouse reminds him of Wilma. He told me she was half coyote. They used to walk together in the trees when he was a boy. Wilma loved it out there. She would run with her back legs hopping like a rabbit. When she had puppies, she went into the woods to make a den inside a fallen tree. He still missed that dog— although his sister was probably right when she said Wilma was all-coyote. Somehow this story ends in tragedy. He didn't go into it, just hinted at it. By the time she was old, Wilma had to be carried up to his room in the attic. She'll be leaving us soon, his mother told him. Anytime he sees trees like these, he says he wants to go in and look around. He might find another Wilma in there.

On a COUNTRY ROAD

An old pickup belongs on the farm, parked in the folded grass of a driveway or making passage between the rows of corn on a country road. An engine loud as black coffee, and every ripple on the road makes the seat squeak like a nest of tin birds. We spot the weasel just ahead, running right beside the tar, its body hunched almost rolling, like a half-inflated inner tube. It's going quick, but as we pass, we see it turn its head to glare. Caught in its mouth is a burly field mouse and what a sudden, fierce look that weasel gives us, startling and sharp as a wound, just before it cuts into the crop it knows by heart.

ALLISON

Be a friend to her and she will remind you. She stops to nuzzle every flower. A walk with her can take an afternoon, but it's sunny and we have all day. Following her lead, you smell them too and just the wonder that they've been here all along is enough to enlighten you. Wake up, she already flew, you have to hurry to catch up. Right now, we're stopped near a convenience store. A parking lot can be a playground where you chase her back and forth until you're tired and laughing. Have you forgotten what that's like? There she is, go over, by the wild rose that climbs the fence and hangs every flower like a cup to sip nectar from.

MISSISSIPPI FROG

It's only very late at night or an early hour of the morning when I hear a frog out there in the yard. My attention between dreams isn't long. I can just spare seconds before the sound of that creaking paddlewheel in the damp leaves becomes a hurdy-gurdy on the corner. Look! Under the cherry tree, a frog in a battered top hat and worn blue suit playing songs of lazy sunshine.

A YELLOW SNAIL

mesmerizing
polished shell
like a wet taxi

when we return
it's still there
waiting for a fare

parked on cement
big drops of rain
we fall to our knees
and get in

The BARN OWL

The wind swept across the big pond behind the barn. An invisible river blew between the poplars out by the road and waved the tall grass aside like green long-bottom weeds. When it hit the barn, warped and worn by the rain, crooked boards faded silver as fish skin, there was a music in the creaks and ticks. The steady hiccup of a rope that hung from a rafter. Up in the broken roof slat, an owl was dreaming his flight above nighttime fields full of mice. He could turn into air silently. But wise as the owl was, he didn't know he slept while the wind blew. He was in a dream apart from everything. He forgot he was also in this world, held together precariously and waiting for that one last breath to fall.

LAKE ERIE SEAHORSES

Somewhere along this lake in the 1950s was a roadside store. It was filled with those things summer tourists love to buy. Most amazing of all, on the wall was a fish tank filled with living seahorses. It was easy for the children stopping there to believe they could run to the shore and scoop a bucket through Lake Erie in hopes of catching their own.

DOREEN

Doreen has a trapdoor that takes her to the roof. At 4 AM, she goes up there, long hair snapping with electricity, and she stands in the rumble of lake thunder, holding the weather tight to her like a crumpled paper bag filled with the flashes of lightning bugs.

The ZENOBIA AIRPORT

Let's assume we know about butterflies. Look how they flutter. Some girl on Zenobia Road sits by her window and cuts each one out of paper. She paints their wings, winds them up, and lets them fly. She spends every moment of the day making something this beautifully, utterly absurd.

CHAMPION the WONDER HORSE

He's a famous movie star, why wouldn't I let him inside? I open the screen door and next thing I know he knocks over the coffee table and now he's eating the curtains off the window.

PLACES to HIDE

They released two tigers down at the end of 32nd Street, where all the new apartments are. It wasn't hard for the tigers to adapt. There was plenty to eat. Places to hide. In a year there were six more of them.

The USED BELUGA

The aquarium was going out of business, each window had a price tag label. A lot of animals were already sold. I thought about getting a seal but I was too late. People were running from tank to tank. I was lucky to find a starfish at a reasonable cost.

15

Not many people believe in them, let alone have one in their possession and then decide to let it go. The porch door opened and a girl stood there in pale sunlight. She looked across the yard, the fallen hand-sized yellow leaves, towards the woods that grew thick behind the house. For fifteen years she kept a unicorn in her room.

The WITCH'S DOG

Neither one of them could touch water. It burned their skin. "I'm sorry," she told her dog. "You'll have to stay indoors." So the dog stood by the window and watched that gray sky and waited all day for it to dry.

The DRAGONFLY JUNKYARD

A weedy lot stacked with the remains of old dragonflies. Broken wings are leaned against the fence like rows of stain glass windows. Motors with the gears pulled out. The long, rusted segments of fuselage. The man who works here says to look around, there are enough parts about to mix and match and put another dragonfly in the air.

The LOST CAT

Think of all the lives that come and go on this planet. One of them was a kitten that found me in the night. Of course I picked it up and held it in my arms but I didn't feel I could hold it forever. I was just as alone without a home, and having a cat along seemed like more than I could handle then. California made stars overhead and I walked around in the dark asking people I met if they lost a cat.

The TIGER HUNTER

Every summer my grandparents had a garden that turned into a jungle. I helped do a little weeding and harvesting, but mostly I was responsible for locating tigers. I would look anywhere the milkweed crept in among the sweet-peas, corn and chard. They liked to pounce from those tall green stalks. I had a jar stuffed with leaves and when I found a striped black and yellow caterpillar, I had to be quick to catch it before it leaped.

The RIGHT BIRD

She needs to step on the dappled light and touch every tree like a friend. It's not something she can keep to herself. Now I find myself doing it too. The moss on the alder, the glow in the leaves. And when we hear a bird that sounds like a parakeet, we both stop to listen.

CONTEMPLATING

The one cloud in the blue sky is actually a goldfish. A girl with a crayon drew it that way. When she held the piece of paper up, the fish floated off. It paddles in the air above the cottonwood trees, contemplating, wary of the steeple and telephone wires.

CHESHIRE CAT in TRAINING

When they're just beginning, it takes effort to balance. A branch seems awful high in the air and it's not just sitting they need to do. This one was only a kitten and it faded in and out with every tentative step. A smile was something it could only manage when the job was done.

The FAKE DOG

We were at the park when I saw the fake dog. At least that's what I told the kids. I pointed out the odd way it ran. They weren't sure. It was obvious to me anyway there was a person inside. Finally, I had to know for certain. I crossed the playing field. Big footprints have flattened the clover, but the fake dog was done running. It was sitting on a bench reading the newspaper.

A HORSE NAMED CARL SANDBURG

An old white horse is riding the elevator of the Leopold. Nobody knows how it ended up in there. The crowd in the lobby watches the arrow as it rises between the floors. For a moment it rests on the 11th floor, then it's moving two stories down, then somewhere else again. By night the people have gone, except for the clerk at the desk who has grown used to it.

SPARROWS

Early on a California morning, she is holding a watering can, reaching above her head to the flower basket. There are two of them. When one is full, she tends the other. The water drains through and rains on the dry cement sidewalk. Some silver pools have formed. As soon as she goes back in the café, the sparrows appear.

The PAINTED HEART

I drove uphill on 50th next to the zoo, this was years ago. Below one of the underpasses, a girl was painting the cement wall. Gigantic bright flowers and stars and animals. I didn't know a heart could jump like that, suddenly all I wanted to do was fall in love with her and color the world with her if only I could stop the car and get out.

The OWL and

The pea-green boat in the light of the moon came sailing, finally sailing back home. The honey and money were long since gone, no more dancing in the tidal zone. The stars still shine the same old way, the sail is gently blown, but although the boat was built for two, the owl is all alone.

RECURRING BIRD

On Telegraph Road at the end of the day, the sidewalk sparrows line her way. They chatter and watch from the leaves. To live among us in poverty, to speak in parables and poetry, to reach out with a healing touch. She is our recurring bird. Her song is no secret, it's something we turn over and over like a prayer. In dark times we remember she is here. To stay in someone's heart is immortality.

The DEER TRAIL

We stop to examine the deer trail, the dog smelling low to the ground, while I look at their flattened path, how it moves along the ridge of the hill, and the tall buttercups that must brush them as they walk through, painting them with yellow light.

A WALRUS

I have never seen a walrus in the field. I'm sure the thought never crossed my mind before. Yesterday, it would have been a complete surprise to me if I saw one, but now I'm prepared...I feel like I'm just waiting to see a walrus.

OUR OWN FIELD

A young deer in our backyard, not much bigger than our dog, it wobbles, it wears white spots that bounce in the dew and spill towards the blackberry, not in any danger from us, safe in our own field.

The RABBIT WATCHERS

They stand in the field, a big group of them, all ages, holding binoculars and cameras. The guide leads them closer to a thicket and that's where they spot their first rabbit. Ears poke above the weeds. The excitement flutters. Then someone points, "Look! There's another!"

EELGRASS

In the Meadows River, the sound of an outboard motor. The boat carves through the channels, little islands, some no more than shoals, poke from the water. Coming up is Marsh Monkey Island. They chatter in the pine and look how they like to swing and throw mussel shells. The shallows are a field of eelgrass. The motor stops. The hush as the hull rushes over the weeds and skates up the stones onto land.

SNAIL

So I go back and forth all day, back and forth drawing lines on the ground the way a snail will do when it runs on worries and I grow accustomed to the rocks and lilies on the path.

The BUMBLEBEE

Every morning she crossed Fielding Avenue on her way to the Wendy's to work. She had a funny way of humming when she took someone's order. Hamburger, fries, soft drink, would set her off like a bumblebee.

The BROKEN BIRD

It repeats the same song on our fence, over and over like listening to an old friend tell a story you've heard again and again. You know where it's going, you know what will be said, but there's something so calming about it that time itself has been lulled and circles around it like a clock.

SEVENTH FLOOR

Next to a fir tree is a small gravestone: "Here Lies Birdy, Wilson's Warbler & Friend." I've buried my share of rabbits and birds and our family dog. Why do we do that, with a flower on top? We hope that space in the ground will lead like an elevator to another, even better place, where there won't be the worries of this world. And when it's your turn, you can see that little yellow warbler again, just listen for: "Seventh Floor... sunshine, running stream, warm breeze, Birdy."

The CAPYBARA

A bit before midnight I got up and looked out the window and saw a strange animal on the grass, near the curb. It was tense as if sniffing the air. It was too small to be a deer, but not a dog, the shape was wrong. I guessed it might be a capybara. I don't know how one drifted so far north on a hot July night. The thermal conditions must have been just right. It stayed an animal for eight more seconds then I realized it wasn't. On 32nd Street in that very spot is a fire hydrant, so tame we almost forget it is there.

The BLACKBERRY CASTLE

Only a rabbit can get through the defenses. A low tunnel is chewed into the thorns, over the bits of a broken ladder that crashed and tangled long ago. Moving on, winding through the rusted cone of a bucket someone filled with berries and dropped by accident. Birds will find a notch between thorns and become radios. Twenty feet into the blackberry castle, there's a clearing. In the middle, a steamer trunk stands on end. Only the rabbit can see Sleeping Beauty projected in the beveled glass window. While she sleeps, she makes the pink flowers turn, green, then ripen into fruit. In another month blackberries will cover the castle walls.

TO BE BEAUTIFUL

Imagine the nerve it takes to be a deer in this town. To wake up somewhere hidden each day, then to be obvious and also to melt in, to be prey, to be beautiful and almost innocent, with a spotted baby to care for, crossing roads to look for something that doesn't seem to exist, getting used to grief, to cling to the idea of a peace that doesn't seem to exist except in the pure joy of sunlight and shade in the leaves, and the miracle of finding flowers in a garden someone forgot to cover with a fence.

PACIFIC WRENS

They go up and down the branch and call to me like distant rusty wheels. So small I could put all three of them in my shirt pocket and walk down the hill like a saint, spreading the music of a faint memory. Remember 1962, when Elvis rode the monorail on the blue night skyline above the streets of the World's Fair and sang a Seattle lullaby.

A DUCK

She wants to come back as a duck. If there's any chance when this life is over, if there are street signs to follow on the other side, or buttons to press, if there's any way she can possibly choose, that's what she wants to be. She's been practicing too—she can make a flawless quack. And it will be such a wonderful new life she insists, water and land will be her home, and she can fly too, and best of all a duck never needs anything more than the world it is born into.

A CAT

There's a cat who lives on campus. I've seen him twice this week as I ride my creaking bicycle. Yesterday morning he ran sleek in front of me chased by two crows into the tall garden leaves.

The GIRL WHO is the RIVER

The girl who is the river would show up where we gathered to play hide-and-seek games in the park or run with us like birds in the field. Sometimes just walking along somewhere, she would be there. She might appear randomly at your yard, her brown hands on the fence, wearing soaking clothes, muddy and torn at the edges. You never knew how long she would stay—if she would be full of energy, or daydreaming and slow and she would only be with us for a minute and go.

HUCKLEBERRIES

Going for a walk in the Chuckanut Hills and true to its name, it's mostly uphill. Looking for huckleberries, only found three or four berries. It's not their season yet. Everything calm and in place where it belonged, from the tops of the trees down the mossy bark to the ghost mushrooms and little yellow flowers. Searching as we hiked along, it was only the huckleberries I couldn't find. In all that green, thinking of jobs off through those leaves down the steep sides of fern and cedar and fir, it's a far way to where people rush around like ants. The other day I watched a crew laying tar. I was thinking about looking for a better job. When it will arrive and where is not that different than me up here looking for huckleberries.

A BAT

evening coming on
we stop when
a bat appears

pedaling the air
almost frantic
to stay aloft

the last rays of sun
stretched taut
in its wings

A RABBIT

our dog stops
still as she gets
hoping to match
heartbeats
with the animal
she can't help
bolting at

A COYOTE

Even though
they're so quiet
you wouldn't know
coyotes are living
in the trees
across the street.

At 4 AM
when the coal train
rumbles through
the horn sets off
a coyote sobbing
giving itself away

CROWS

crows
spilled out
around
a garbage can

OVER MILKWEED

The air is rare above the milkweed field. Swallows glide across the hot afternoon. The wildflowers open and close with the sun, stars and moonlight, the whippoorwill wakes in the tree. This island of milkweed is its own little world, but something is happening, too fast to stop. Past a cow on the other side of the old stone wall…another cow too…then a little further off, where the field is clawed away, new houses have been built almost overnight. The way those houses are growing and spreading closer, it looks like the meadow is only one more memory in the way of something hungrier and bigger and always looking for more. Once the milkweed grew in acres and they drilled the stalks and carried the milk in buckets to the edge of the lane where horse-carts would take them into town.

A COUPLE MORNINGS this WINTER

The fog reaches up the hill from the ocean like the tide. Detective weather, clouds on the ground, washing around everything. Ordinary sounds echoed and carried for blocks. Long forgotten sea anemones are sprouting crayon colors out of the cracks in cement. The bus is a whale with glowing yellow eyes swimming up the incline.

FURNITURE

In February, nights started getting cold again
the house roots creaked with a moaning wind
coming from the starry clear sky.
Awake in bed, I heard the door downstairs
open and shut again quietly followed by
a clicking about on the kitchen floor.
"Another deer?" I wondered.
The moon keeps letting them in,
they're like furniture wandering around.
I had to know for certain, down
the steep stairs to the kitchen
dark as pulled over cotton.

POSIE CRUTCHFIELD in:
UNTIL the COWS COME HOME

The city woke up in the falling snow. Rattling bottles, a milk truck slid to a stop in front of the tenement house. In the gray blue light, Posie Crutchfield carried a basket of bottles to the door, left them like bowling pins, and went back to the truck. She turned the key. There was an engine bang and a burst of black smoke coughed into the cold air. Her eyes rolled at her fate. She crunched into the snow again and kicked the tire. It was no good. Something caught her eye on the other side of the fence slats, moving on four legs, ringing a bell. It mooed at her. Posie's eyes lit up with piano keys as she led the cow from its yard and hooked it to the milk truck. Now she could finish her rounds on time. She patted the cow's side. The city didn't have long to wait, while she walked the cow from block to block and brought them milk in the snow.

MILK WHITE SKY
FLECKED with BIRDS

A cat sitting
in the window
like a pitcher
you could pour
into a bowl

POSIE CRUTCHFIELD in:
The LAUREL & HARDY LIBERATION ARMY

Posie Crutchfield, very old on a black creaking bicycle, turned down an alley and rattled cobblestones. She rode onto a two-by-four slanting up onto scaffolding framing a brick building. Like a sparrow hopping branches in a bare winter tree, she went up and up to the very top where she stopped. A hundred feet from the ground, she pushed the bike up on its kickstand so the back wheel was free to spin. She opened the box latched onto the handlebars, revealing a gleaming silver and green projector. She fed a reel of black film into the spool and set the switch, pulled a string, then pedaled the movie into rolling. A little candle yellow lightbulb was glowing. Across the drop, images and slogans magically appeared on the opposite wall. Above the roofs and traffic, the cold city, tired and dark and gray from long winter days, was given a chance to see Laurel and Hardy comedies.

MIKE'S BIRDHOUSE

We would ride to where
the concrete of the city
broke off into the bramble
banks of the Columbia
park our bicycles
under the freeway

The highway roared
pyloned up overhead
factories and warehouses
beside the dumpster

We had to climb its side
and pry open the door
to get inside and
what a sight
to behold

As daylight fell in
we echoed all over
the cut pine scraps
stacking our hands full
it was a sort of paradise
at a time when I used to

make toys and boxes
and giraffes five feet tall

I built a nest in the basket
on my black one-speed
Mike filled his backpack
then we rode Hawthorne home

As if filmed by timelapse
over the next few hours
we made birdhouses

They were strange
we made them that way
mine never left the bookshelf
Mike took a porcupine vision
spiny with nails
up into the eaves

It didn't seem possible
that pointed contraption
would collect any birds
the air was too big
the city was so wide

When they did arrive
like watching a cartoon
in a little wooden television
a pair of sparrows

found Mike's birdhouse
stuffing it with weeds
to cushion the nails
and the Spring filled it
with their family

RABBIT STRING

When the rabbit
leaves in the grass
only one tall stalk
is left trembling

a string of music
only I can hear
this morning

ALL SHAKESPEARE'S BIRDS

Edward Shepherd stepped out of the elevator carrying a suitcase filled with birds. After the cold winter air of Lima, Ohio, the sudden warmth of the red planet hit him like a wave. He wore his best tan seersucker suit. He swung the suitcase lightly as he stepped onto Mars.

This was his second trip to Mars. The first time, half a year ago, he'd been struck by the bare violet sky, awfully empty. He took it upon himself to change that. When he went back to America, he grabbed every bird he could, collecting pigeons, sparrows, starlings, crows and more. They weren't just random birds picked from trees and telephone wires—he brought only the birds mentioned in the plays of Shakespeare. That was Edward's mission, the reason for this second trip to Mars.

The elevator door slid closed behind him. He walked across the sand toward a hill. His alligator shoes slid into the loose soil.

At the top of the climb, he stopped. This was where it would start. He pictured a statue of himself placed here, and the birds that would land on him. He opened the suitcase and there were the Earth birds, dehydrated and kept in packets.

This PENNYLAND

Spotted
two deer
on the hillside
this morning

Something
I like to see
a reminder
from beyond
this pennyland

MR. FRITZ'S BUG

Observing the flights that raced across his retina, Mr. Fritz finally eased out of his hammock. He had nothing else to do this lazy day. First, he put a thick lens invention in front of his eye. The world jumped with details. He fine-tuned the box all the wires ran to. The connection created vision made of horizontal lines that he could follow like yarn left behind in a maze. Taking up the fading thread of one, he pursued it across the field, along the dazzling wall of garden flowers to where it landed on mossy bark of an old elm tree. He tuned the dials to see more clearly what was happening on the trunk. The line ended in a little green bug who had flown all the way here. It waved its six legs to another bug it met and Mr. Fritz had to zoom in close for this astonishment. The bug whose life he chose to chase, pulled out a blur of something and had it punched in the smallest machine. It passed the timecard to another bug, who then counted out frail scales of money. Mr. Fritz's bug stuffed them under its wing and sprang with a joy off back into the wind.

The RADIO-CONTROLLED CROW

Unfortunately, nobody believed me when I told them about the radio-controlled crow. Twice, while I stood outside the Museum of Science and Industry, it flew over. On its back, between its wings, it carried what looked like a walkie-talkie, long antenna extending out over its tail. For a while it landed and walked back and forth on the roof gutter, but by the time anybody else showed up, it strolled off into territory hidden from the parking lot view. Still, it's a little strange that people coming out of there, after seeing hoop wheels, dynamos, miniature towns, reconjured canneries, hydroplanes and flying boats, Rainier Beer and Bobo the stuffed gorilla, could possibly doubt the existence of the radio-controlled crow.

POE ECHO

I can't see him
but I can hear him
off through far
carved up woods
a raven calling
another answering

END of STORY

"No more yelling!" he thundered into the dark bedroom where his daughter's bunkbed loomed in a shroud. "I don't want to hear from you again unless a gorilla's arm comes through that window and shakes you like a ragdoll. Now goodnight."

WAITING for the END of STORY

Ten blocks away, two hairy arms were holding a newspaper up like a shower curtain. Behind all those words, a gorilla was chewing on a cigar. He dropped the paper and lifted his left arm to look at all the wristwatches he was wearing. They all read about 9:30. After he took a sip from the styrofoam coffee cup on his desk, he reached out for the ringing telephone. Through trick-photography, the ape appears to talk into the phone. "Hey... Really?... Well, call me if it happens again, okay?... Yeah, I'll be waiting here." Then he dropped the phone back in the cradle. He reached for a pack of cigarettes on the table.

LIKE SPARROWS FOLLOWING HIM
WHEREVER HE WENT

Like sparrows
Following him
Wherever he went

Getting caught
On branches
And corners

Hopping down
On sidewalks
Like falling rain

POE at the ZOO

He must have started on a folded scrap
with a sharpened charcoal or a nib in hand
making observations, leaning on the metal rail
at the Paris Zoo ape house…Brute strength
a razor and a chimneyed thought, trailing words
storied out beyond the city limits like clouds.

BIRDSONGS

The radios played birdsongs, from the latest thrill to the warbling old tunes your grandparents knew. Even the shop on the corner would have one or two wooden cages in eaves to speaker out music while you buy coffee for the trip on the morning trolley. Wintering cold with a warm cup in hand, that last pretty song would stick in your head while you went.

The VOICE of AMERICA BIRD

It was supposed to be a sort of weapon, aiming for those antennas on the other side of the border. What would happen if they heard the Duke Ellington Orchestra or Elvis Presley sing? What happens when Nina Simone puts on her wings, when she flies over fences, landmines, cement and soldiers and finds someone like you?

The LUCKY HALIBUT

It sat in a lavender glow
neon and flashing window lights
the bubbles around it were frantic
the glass of its tank hummed
with strange delight

The Lucky Halibut was painted
on the sign, but nobody knew
what made it lucky or even if
it could bring luckiness to you

So there is sat, unknown in the sand
flat, held down by gallons of water
with a secret or not

The UGLY CAT

The porch became its home day after day
and nights too. Not because it was getting
food or the best shelter in the neighborhood.
The whole thing was a mystery to Martin.
He didn't know what to do.
The ugly cat attached itself to
the wood sills of the porch like
a barnacle with crooked eyes.

PHINNEAS

Slow padded feet
take him down a path
green grass and pine overhead
leafy maples dapple light
across the fur on his back.
Fur like dandelion fluff
Phinneas follows his old lady
through the rock fence cleft
crackling fallen leaf slow decent
to the place where land breaks.
Rocks lead sharply to the sea
a sandy little cove
where they sit together
to rest bones and be alive.
The tide is eternal
anytime of day
the water is here
or on the way.

This is WHO

So this is who walks around at 2 AM
in the neighborhood all blacked out
except for the tall amber street lamps
spaced every block and a half
I'm out walking the baby
in charge of wide-eyed insomnia
when the leaves of the willow
rattle behind us and ahead
a rabbit darts over the street
silent as a dream going home
to sleeping home

BESSEMER

Adapting
to the air
since 1853
butterflies and bees
wear
soot wings
to gather
charcoal clover
blossoming
by the glow
of bessemer

SLOW GAME

The town is back again
familiar names and neighbors
laid out in grass avenues

alive with the wind
warm sunlight and the far off
sounds of music and cars

all the stones
tip and slant
like a slow game
of dominoes

a dust coated cat
wakes on the weeds
trolleys off to hunt
among the slate

three

WHO WOULDN'T WANT A GORILLA MASK?

One warm summer evening in Ohio
I was at Goodwill and saw a gorilla mask.
I didn't have any money on me,
I was wearing a tourist costume
shorts and a pocketless shirt
but I thought I could return
in the morning to buy it.
So I stepped back into the crickets
and twilight, thinking of all the things
I could do with that gorilla mask.
It never occurred to me there was
someone else, someone with $5
entering the store at that moment.
As I was crossing the wide parking lot
walking in the weeds next to the road,
someone was pulling that mask down
off the wall and holding it like a flower.

TWO MOURNING DOVES

One is sitting
on the wire
another arrives
whirring wings

It's evening
they could fly
anyplace
but this
is where
they stay

NOAH ROAD

His path to the sea
took him past the house
with the barking dog

He could understand
that kind of urgency
the dog only wanted
to be taken along

He had a wooden boat
overturned on the sand
the oars were stored
like candlesticks inside

UNSTUNG

Sunday morning
through the woods
into meadows

a sunflower tree
deep grass dew

wading into fall
the sour breeze
under curling leaves
plums and apples
on the ground

the last fruit
for hornets
too busy
to sting

MOTH

A moth upon
your wooden door

a knock so soft
you wouldn't know

The NIGHTWATCHMAN at the BRONX ZOO

All the stories that aren't written down, the things that happened we will never know. His thermos would rest on top of the locker while he changed out of his uniform at the break of dawn.

POE in JAPAN

He took a skeleton with sails over the Pacific, crashed through two bad storms when he prayed for the end, then in a gray morning stood at the rail to see the skyline turn into land. Japan. Soon he saw the pagoda towers, the pines, the wooden houses, pennants of fish, dragons, bright creatures that kited on the air. When he stepped ashore, all covered in black, he wobbled from lack of ground for so long. He knew he was being looked at, he felt the picture frame on him. He wore it awkwardly up past the fishing things beside the shore. He hoped to find an address someone gave him. The whole reason for the journey was scratched across in his tree branch writing on a torn scrap of paper he kept caught like a dove in a pocket. When looking for somewhere in a place like this, he was just another wind blown off the sea, someone who looked lost as a ghost.

BELLS

I break
two branches
and the chickadees
ring like bells
in the pine

SOME SPARROWS

some sparrows
picked through dust

this passing bicycle
sends them up

gray stones
hold down
the spot they left

The BULL

They tried
to keep us out
told us stories
about the bull
but every time
we snuck
into the field
we never saw
any sign of him

SNOW WHITE MOTH

holding the concrete wall
thoughts turned off
calm as snow

The SACRED HEART JUNKYARD

that orange van
with the holy icon
Mike painted on
should have been
put in the garden
across the street
kept hidden by
the St. Francis church
instead of where
it ended up
punished
by a punk band
who ran it down
on the highway
abandoned and towed
to another kind of garden
where motors don't run
then again
maybe that's okay
that face with crown
and burning heart
holding hands out
and comforting
continues
looking out
for the flock

DREAMS

Is it rain doves that call
from far over hills
The nighttime is haunted
by firefly wings
Whatever it is
Wherever you are
What's hiding is
never as far
as it seems

A FROG

The cashier has a frog
in her throat
a long day is ending
at last

The sky is empty

When she gets home
before she sleeps
she puts the frog
in a china cup
beside her bed

WAKING UP the OWL

Starting night
burning newsprint
cardboard, letters
and wrapping paper
sent up a yellow
sheet of fire

Little cities
orange lights
tumble in thick
smoke curl

Finally
waking up the owl
like a piece of moon
in the barn
taking flight

CLOVER

so little
you sat
on the curb
with your legs
in the Ohio wind

HERMAN the FLY

lace curtains
for a screen door
see the oak tree
and the willow
the neighborhood
the blue sky
and the breeze
opens a space
for Herman
to fly in

SUMMER GREEN

the whole field
is summer green
and honeybees
tend the flocks
of white clover

The MERMAID RELOCATION PROGRAM

Someone discovered her in the reservoir,
sometimes it happened in a swimming pool
there were also lakes and ponds and streams.
A red truck drove there. They caught her
and put her in a tank in the back. It was
still early, the day was gray and cold as a
submarine They took her to the ocean and
parked, lifted her down. All that water poured
out, she went with it, in the flood from the
bin. This happened so often they could make
their living from it.

At LAST, the YEAR 1923

Andrew always wore a cardigan and like a mother kept the monkey safe in there. Going up country, his pet caused a stir riding in the open touring car. Arriving in New Hampshire, swimming in the river cooling off, Jane's white legs were nipped underwater. At last, the year 1923, when Andrew died, his dearest friend cried and cried. A broken heart, alone, so sad without him. It must seem like a dream to realize such things happening. Once upon an afternoon the family would gather at the zoo to go see Jocko and so remember Andrew.

FOLLOW YOUR FRIEND

Follow your friend on
the crop that isn't

This is a field of mud
each step up
needs somewhere
to land

Try not to sink
when you come down

Your friend left
prints hollowed
with heels of water

The MINIATURE COW

He will be three in 8 days and what he really wants is a cow. A cow his size. I'm not sure how that will happen. I've been watching for one. Finding one isn't easy, but I have an idea. On Guide Meridian, alongside the road before the parking lot starts, there's cattails and blackberry and on the corner an old fencepost from the days when this was farmland. That's where I expect to find a miniature cow. Anyone watching from passing traffic would think it was only a dog looking out.

DANDELIONS

Gypsum made dandelions grow all over the lush green grass. It wasn't a difficult conjuring, not after four years at Magic Island. He sat on a rock and thought of bringing the flock all the way down to the beach. Dandelions don't like getting too close to the sea. That saltwater stings and they've heard stories of the strange plants underwater. Kelp and weeds. Barnacles and anemones. Whales bigger than a house. He got up and the dandelions followed along with him, down the steps to the shore. The flowers hissed and bumped into each other on the rocks, but they hurried to catch up with him, running on their roots across the sand, and before he walked into the shallows, they quickly floated under his feet to make a yellow raft.

BIRD LANGUAGES

The classroom windows were open
to let their voices out. Bird Languages
was being taught. Ms. Rollins had them
working on American Robin, Northwest dialect.
She chirped the diagram on the blackboard
and turned to her students. Their echo
took off, left the window and flew.

SUMMER AIR

Low swallows
over a lulled field

Our daughter and son
go running to catch them

Their veer and swerve
like comedy
in the summer air

racing a bee
downhill
my bicycle wins

one crow
on top of the fir
sees more than we do

tilling the soil
the crows pop up
along the rows

fog so thick
a cat can walk
on top of it

on Quarry Road
the car just misses
a yellow butterfly

MOURNING DOVES

They perch
on power lines
so their sorrows
are magnified
carried for miles

Far down the wire
someone will cry
and won't know why

The BEEKEEPER of FRANKLIN DRIVE

It was going to rain
on Franklin Drive
the sky continues
that familiar gray lake
coloring an old man
sighed into a chair
who shuffles bees
for solitaire

*the wonderful
stupid man*

The BIRDWATCHERS of AKRON

The birdwatchers of Akron first reported it in the Beacon Journal. Someone was painting black iron crosses on cardinals. They had been spotted by several people. The red birds would glide in low out of the cold gray sky. The newspaper offered a reward for anyone getting a photograph. Around the birder's table at Denny's on their usual Thursday morning, that was all they could talk about. Unanimously, the Akron Birders Association decided they needed a detective to solve the bird mystery.

Ernie Nelson gulped his coffee and stammered, "What kind of maniac would paint on a beautiful bird?"

The others at the table looked glumly at their plates. Not much was left. Vera still had a half piece of rye bread toast that everyone kept eyeing.

"You don't need a detective! I'll find this monster myself."

"Come on Ernie…"

"Be calm, Ernie. This is a job for a professional."

But Ernie held up his hands like a saint. "Give me two days. I'll find the monster."

When Ernie left the restaurant a few minutes

later, he felt like an Atlantic Tern. He grinned and breathed the air and soared over the tar. On the horizon it looked like it was going to rain.

His car was waiting. He inherited it from his grandmother. A mustard yellow 1972 Duster. He liked it. He believed it gave him a TV detective look when he drove it around.

He let himself in. The car started after a couple of tries. It's these cold mornings, he thought, I'm the same way. Before he set the car moving, he dialed the radio to find some good music.

He got on West Market Street and drove. As the city got lower, he watched the sky, the grids and lines of telephone wires and the birds on them. He counted flocks of crows and followed those swerving patterns the starlings make.

He would let his instinct guide him. Two days gave him plenty of time.

Plus, he knew a few things about cardinals— for example, he knew the range of a cardinal's territory. He already thought this thing out. After talking with three of the witnesses, he put his high school math to good use. Plotting the intersection of the three sightings placed the cardinals in the Fairlawn district.

To avoid a bad song, he turned the station and hit the Don McChord update. Ernie was instantly smiling at that gravelly old voice on the radio. For sixty years Don McChord had been announcing the news. Ernie was just in time to hear the reporter wrap it up.

"And finally, in Akron, Ohio…Can you believe a new bird has been discovered? It's got the local birdwatchers scratching their heads. See, it looks like a cardinal, but it has the markings of the Red Baron's plane. This is Don McChord and that's the news today."

Ernie turned the radio off. He rolled the window down. Half interested he spotted a pair of mourning doves on a TV antenna. He couldn't believe it—Don McChord had used their bird situation for the joke at the end of the report.

He stopped at the traffic light on Trunko Road. Drumming his fingers on the wheel, he waited for the green. A blue jay hopped across the top of someone's fence. He was really giving the sky the once over now, looking for red as bright as the traffic light over the road. It was about time to park and take it on foot. He kept binoculars in his glovebox.

When the car behind Ernie honked its horn, he steered the Duster straight for two blocks then took a left, into the side streets. He wanted trees, big yards, bird feeders. Samuel's house was nearby. Vera lived down this way too…She probably saved that toast for her birds, wrapped it in napkin…He kind of liked Vera, he'd been to her house a few times for tea and talk about migrations. He was thinking about her as a flash of red shot across the street. Too late, it was gone into branches around a blue house. It was time to park.

He pulled in beneath a big chestnut tree. There were sparrows on the branches, by summer this would be a deep green-shaded pool. He grabbed his binoculars and got out.

It was a quiet street, bird songs, the clack of an aluminum ladder some guy was setting up against his house. Ernie was close to a cardinal, he could feel it.

He drew the binoculars around his neck and started walking. He whistled a cardinal call and tried it again. It was better the second time. He paused to listen for an echo. Birdwatching meant being a detective, having powers of deductive reasoning and a long knowledge of the subject to draw on.

The ladder creaked as the man on it turned to ask Ernie, "You looking for something?"

"Oh." Suddenly he felt suspicious, standing there on the cement with binoculars. "I'm looking for cardinals."

The man took a step down the ladder.

Ernie cracked a smile. "You probably have a pretty good view up there."

"I read that story in the paper too," said the man on the ladder. "Are you after the reward?"

"No. I'm…Actually, I'm trying to find the

person who painted the cardinals. I'm a detective."

"Uh-huh." The ladder creaked again. He pointed, "Well, you might start by looking around the corner there."

"Okay. Thanks. I will."

Something flickered by in the air. Ernie twitched. It was only a yellow finch. It did look like a toy airplane though. He could almost understand why someone would paint them that way.

He followed the cracked pavement, turned on the next street, watching all the places a bird could be. A lane of cherry trees lined the street, their pink blossoms were only a day or two in unfolding. He wondered if that was why the man on the ladder had sent him this way, to see this postcard of Spring arriving after the long cold Ohio winter. He paused. There were sparrows hopping in the branches.

Then, it was exactly like one of those television programs, his breath caught, he could almost hear the fanfare as time seemed to freeze the moment. He had discovered the final clue that broke the cardinal mystery.

There was a wooden sign hung to the gate of a yard.

I Paint Anything
Houses, Pictures
Birds

And as if directed with bird choreography, a

cardinal dropped out of a tree and landed on the lawn. It tucked its painted wings to its sides.

In less than an hour Ernie had found the place. He felt like the hero in a short story by Raymond Chandler...stepping from the umbrella of new cherry blossoms, pushing open the wooden gate, walking on the slate of flagstones towards the culprit's house.

Actually, he hadn't prepared a victory speech. At breakfast, he pictured himself catching the sallow-looking artist. Now that he was here, the fight had gone out of him, his temper had cooled. Also, he didn't expect to find himself in a garden like this. He slowed to a stop on the path so he could stare and take everything in. A museum was grown around him.

"Hi, Ernie!"

He knew her voice, though in his head he just couldn't picture her being here, until he saw her, standing on the porch.

"You really are a detective," Vera laughed. She stepped down into the grass next to a tiger sculpture made from strips of tin. "Do you know Charles Deloney?"

"No." Ernie watched the front door open, and a big curly haired man walked onto the porch. His blue overalls were speckled with paint, including red.

"Hey. I'm Chuck."

"Hi," Ernie said. "He's the one who painted the cardinals?" he asked Vera. "Why didn't you tell me?"

She twisted her mouth and looked away.

The artist held up his big hands apologetically, "It was just an idea I had. I stopped painting birds when I heard about the trouble I caused. Sorry."

"Sorry?" Ernie had stuffed his hands in his pockets. The car key fit in his palm. He closed a fist around the key and sighed.

A HUNDRED BIRDS

The storm had finally rolled away. It left a bruise on the horizon when he got to work and surveyed the windy damage. Branches were thrown across the ground and a wire lay down over a roof. He hoped nothing got out of the cages and pens.

The buffalo were there. As he drove by, two monkeys hung to their tree like overripe fruit. Their tire pendulum swung with no one on it. The chickens were feather beaten. The tortoise was a stone in his field. But the giraffe was dead. The thunder must have made it run without enough sense to halt at the fence.

He stopped beside it and turned the engine off. The long shape of the giraffe ran through the weeds like a checkered African river. He would need to do something.

So he did.

Every bump or turn in the road, he looked in the mirror to make sure the trailer was still attached. The giraffe lay heavily across the bed of the truck, all the way to the extremity of the boat trailer where its head dipped sorry opened eyes.

Getting the giraffe to the lake unseen and then backing down into the water to float it away sounded like a dream, but in the new calm light of morning after storm, he met only a few doves on wires watching him. Tall walls of corn on either side sheltered him from farmers' eyes.

He fiddled with the radio dial nervously... Country music, religious monologues and their commercials, but no newsflash reports. He gripped the wheel with both hands and steered the rest of the way there.

The lake shimmered ahead of him. It was wide and deep enough to hide any mystery with waves and silt or carry the pieces to sea. He turned around in the empty parking lot and maneuvered the giraffe towards the boat ramp. Lined up, he shifted the truck again and started to reverse. The water held the wheels when he stomped on the brake.

Children had poured out of the wildflowers and sand to run up and stand next to his door. He cut the motor and greeted them. A wave was all he could manage.

"What's going on?" the first one had to chirp. "Is that a real giraffe?" and "Why is it on your truck?" and very soon the air fairly sang with their questions. It was a hundred birds until their teacher hushed them. She wore binoculars around her neck. She read the message on the green door of his truck and asked, "Are you from the zoo?"

"Yes."

"Maybe you could explain to the children what you are doing."

A girl said, "What will happen to the giraffe?"

"Well…" he stalled. He could hear the water lap at the trailer. He came that close. "This giraffe had an accident in the storm last night."

The children let out a sad chorus.

"Don't worry! It's happened before." He quickly tried again, "It will be alright. I drove him here to dip him in the lake. It's the only thing that works to restore a giraffe."

They stared at him.

"You need a lot of water," he continued. "Everything will be alright though," he waved, "you can go back to your fieldtrip now!"

The teacher laughed. "Oh, I think the children will find this far more interesting than any redwing blackbird." They clamored like a tin marching band.

He tried to smile. He said something under his breath as he restarted the truck. "Why not…" he shrugged.

He turned to watch over his shoulder as he backed the giraffe into the lake.

The silver water rippled over savannah camouflage.

Probably a minute pushed by before he dared to speak. "Sometimes these things take time." It was plain to see how the teacher felt about what her class of eight-year-olds might be witnessing.

"Is the giraffe asleep?" a little voice asked.

He rubbed his forehead to wake any answer that would help.

Nothing.

It didn't matter though.

A splash and four legs thrashing kicked at the trailer and threw the truck from side to side. The giraffe had returned to life and flung itself off into the water. Screaming children scattered as they hid across the weeds and dunes.

He leaped out of the truck cab, falling back in time to catch the breeze and spray of the giraffe crashing past him.

Its tall neck angled off in the air.

He saw it go, in the few seconds it took to disappear over the hill. It left a path riddled with redwing blackbirds.

CLEMENTINE SERPENTINE

The mermaid says, "We have seaweed curtains opening, swimming birds with orange scales and there are neighborhoods of whales. Chinese wrecks at rest on sand, golden pirate coins, caravans of eels with eyes that glow." Then her body curves over sleek green tail fins waves goodbye as she dives underwater to breathe. The light in the tank went dark as soot, the crowd shuffled feet to go past the sleeping glass.

SON of a BEEHIVE

The black and white hum of the China Clipper four-engine flying boat drones in his sleep. His exhaustion carries even into his dreams where he relives the frightening past few days…thrown out of the Queen's palace, the city of workers, chased to the docks where he caught the last flight out. He awakes with a start.

The steward offers a tray of food.

"No thanks…I have my own," he weakly refuses and begs, "Could you pass me that suitcase? There, the yellow one." His narrow arm bent like a willow branch.

"It's sticky," the steward apologizes. "Let me get a towel."

"No, that's alright. Just pass it down."

He snapped the latches, opened up to a gold syrup that fills the insides, dipped his hands in deep, like a magician pulling sunlight from a box.

On the sidewalks and parks of the new city he gathered whatever was ultraviolet and could be turned into honey. He went back and forth all day til the great bags slung over his shoulders were full and the soles of all his shoes were wearing out.

Finally tired. The crows were headed to roosts around Green Lake. He stumbled to the doors of a downtown hotel. The uniformed guard nodded and let him in, onto marble, the gleam of the lobby crowd, over to the elevator that took him up the many stacks of floors to his own almost-empty room. A tablecloth stood in the middle of the floor.

Just to be sure, he sealed the door behind him, poured and shook out what he caught in the gardens, enough of a treasure to start over with.

The PURPLE CAT with GREEN EARS

She appeared in my sleep. She was there to calm between the restless shuffle of dreams as the curtain worried in the draft and shook with the next show setting up.

HORSES

Another summer is gone. The gray is back, the rain machine is starting in gear, the wind is hissing in the tree outside our window at night. With the weight of lead, October is here and what all of this adds up to is that people turn a little desperate. You feel the passing of time, wishes are made.

My wife called the Wish-Maker, it wasn't me. I don't know, sure wishes are nice, but I guess I'm not the type to get all worked up, going to the trouble of arranging for one to be made. Plus, there's all that money thrown away.

I was standing at the window watching the clouds, stirring my cup of instant coffee when there was a knock on the door.

Elizabeth answered it. We were both expecting it, but like I said, she was more excited at the prospect than I was.

"Gandy?" she said.

"That's me," laughed the voice hidden behind the opened door.

"Lenny!" my wife called me, "the Wish-Maker's here!"

I was still watching the clouds. Drifts of them piled up over the islands, it looked like rain on the way.

"Will you come in, Gandy?" Elizabeth said.

"Well, generally speaking I like to do these transactions out of doors."

"Of course! Lenny, I'm going outside. Are you coming?"

"Okay…" I said. "I'll meet you. I'll get my shoes."

She shut the door. Their voices were smudged by the walls and muffling leaves of the thick rhododendron pressed to the house.

I took my coffee cup back to the kitchen, set it on the formica table and fetched my shoes from beside the back door. I had only been home from work for an hour.

Outside, I followed the sound of their voices, around the back of the house on the cracked cement path between the garage to the driveway. Some of the wet spindly flowerless stalks grabbed at me.

I could hear Gandy laughing. In another moment I could see him. He stood leaning against a tall bamboo pole, the end of it up in the air was fitted with the copper lantern that would provide Elizabeth's wish. Gandy himself didn't seem that imposing, dressed in gray sweatshirt and dark jeans. He noticed me and nodded.

My wife was telling him how much this wish meant to us.

I stopped near them and stared up at the Wish-Maker's lantern.

It looked pretty beat up. There were scratches and dents on it like maybe he'd been using it to catch bats with.

"Alright," Gandy said when my wife was finished, "Are you ready?"

"Oh yes!" she cried. She quickly handed him a thick roll of money and he lowered the lantern by slanting the stick uphill.

I've never actually seen one of these lanterns up close before. Elizabeth has done this before. She even credited a Wish-Maker for her finding me. I guess that's possible. I don't know. I suppose a machine could know where I would be at any given time and send me a signal to lock eyes with a girl. Who knows how love begins?

Gandy flipped a latch on the lantern and stuffed the money inside then raised the thing skywards. *Say goodbye to all that dough*, I thought. Elizabeth watched the lantern start to glow, like a girl at a circus show.

Gandy chuckled and said, "This'll be a good one."

Some of the blue-white light buzzed through the cracks in the lantern. It gave a wheeze then with a pop, a spark flew out of the top, turning into a puff of acrid black smoke.

Gandy guffawed.

Elizabeth clapped her hands. I was glad the gently swooping branches of the alder hadn't caught on fire.

"You got your wish," Gandy said.

"Where?" said Elizabeth. "Where is it?"

Gandy squinted and nodded and took in a loud breath of air. "It's over behind your garage." He pointed. "In the backyard…"

"Oh Lenny!" Elizabeth grabbed my arm. "Let's go see!"

"Sure," said Gandy. He laughed again. With his tall walking stick and lantern and charcoal clothes, I got it now—he looked like a woodcut from a Grimm's fairy tale. Someone drawn in the background while the Pied Piper ran off with the children, or a troll guarding a gate to the woods. He was still chuckling as Elizabeth dragged me up the gravel driveway.

It was starting to rain lightly. Maybe there would be something practical waiting for us, I hoped, like a door going to a warmer world.

A blue jay squawked out of our way.

I don't know what Elizabeth was hoping for, but I had my hopes up too, I'll admit. The Wish-Maker put on a pretty good show.

Along the edge of the garage a bright little creek of runoff water rippled downhill. It made a silver sound.

As Elizabeth and I turned the corner, we both

sort of turned to stone. There in our backyard stood the sorriest looking wish I've ever seen. A horse, maybe gray at one time, it was turned to a shade of almost blue. Every angle and edge of it was crooked or bent like it had been crumpled by a big hand. When it turned to look at us, it did so with the cross-eyed gaze of a broken clock.

While I wanted to laugh at the pure absurdity of it, I couldn't. When Elizabeth let go with a sob I put my arm around her. "It's alright," I said. I could feel the rain on my neck as I kissed her hair. I looked over her at the shape in our yard. The rain made dots on the horse like swiss cheese. "It's not that bad…"

Elizabeth wiped at her eyes with the back of her hand.

"I don't know much about horses," I told her, "Maybe that's a good one."

"Yeah, right," she said.

"Well…I do think we should get it out of the rain. Let's put it in the garage?" I didn't know.

Elizabeth agreed. "You do it though."

I said, "Okay." There was a rope looped around the horse's neck. "Hello fellow," I said. It didn't seem to mind my approaching it, or maybe it hadn't seen me yet. Anyway, I got there and took hold of the rope. I wasn't afraid of it, but I didn't know what it was capable of doing. It was like a badly wired electric blanket, shivering wet.

"Okay…Come along…"

I tugged and the horse started to move. I called down the hill, "Hey Elizabeth, do you think you could open the garage door for us?"

She hurried away as I led the horse across the weeds and fallen leaves. It picked up speed. By the time we got to the driveway and started down it, I had adapted to the beast's strangely irregular gait. The frequency had transmitted down the rope into me. Like the horse, my left foot kicked out a little to the side, while my right dragged at the heel.

I heard the big garage door go up with a racket of rusted coasters and my wife's groan. It wasn't easy to move that slab of metal. One of these days I had to fix it.

Fortunately our horse walked right in. Elizabeth pushed the lawnmower aside to make space. It wasn't much of a stall, but how much room did a horse need anyway? Didn't they just stand there? I ran my hand over its damp, rough back to brush off the rain. "Do we put a blanket on it?" I asked Elizabeth. I remember in *Black Beauty*, the horse got wet and they forgot to put a blanket on it and the horse got sick…Or maybe you're not supposed to put a blanket on it? I guess I can't remember…

Elizabeth rubbed at her eyes. "Lenny, I don't know anything about horses." She stared at me desperately. "I don't know what to do! I never should have called that Wish-Maker."

171

She was right, but I wasn't fool enough to say that. The three of us stood there and listened to the rain hit the roof overhead. What were we supposed to do? Later I could take the horse back outside. There was grass in the mossy backyard. I could show it to the mountain of blackberries growing on the property line. Or were blackberries something only a goat would eat?

I sighed and sat down on an overturned bucket. It was only the start of a long season of wind, rain and cold until finally the sun would come back out again. In the meantime, I'm trying to see something golden in what happened. It could be the laughing Wish-Maker Gandy was a lesson after all. We don't know anything about horses yet, but we have all winter to learn.

14
animals

SWALLOWTAIL

It's easy to imagine
that's a little person
with black and yellow
wings attached and a
lifelong love of flowers

The BUMBLING BEE

Anywhere
I see a flower
attracting bees
there's me
bumbling
at beauty

MR. and MRS. SOFT and WARM

A little rabbit crackles in the leaves next to the path. At first I think, what a frozen morning for you to be out, then I realize, I'm the one walking in the cold to a job all day. He's going down a lantern-lit hallway into the warm earth, to lay in the softest nest with a wife all murmured in fur.

The PLASTIC-COATED CAT

Across the wet lawn
the sound of vinyl
gives it away

The COW GHOST

In the new woods, alder trees have sprung up
along the pond during the last thirty years.
All that's left of the dream this used to be a farm
a few posts stuck leaning in blackberry
some ragged screws of barbed wire holding
them together. Seen through the leaves
the houses built twenty years ago steam
in the morning. My dog pauses to smell
and I stop too, knowing it's near.
Close by, the ghost of a cow hovers
in the air.

BLUEBELL the MOLE

Caught by the cat
left in the grass
time for a shovel
put it to rest

cut a piece of earth
lay the dead mole in

those big hands that
dug through the ground
now held out open
in surrender

cover him over
with a blanket of moss
and some bluebells
placed on top

NEIGHBORHOOD STORIES

The deer
are getting
daring

watching
in windows

one goes
up the driveway
eats our flowers
hangs around
acting like
he owns the place

TWO RABBITS

So small
they could fit
in my pockets

SENDING OUT THOUGHTS

My dog and I were walking in the wet woods.
The trail was rained on and the slugs were here
and there. At first I was watching out for them
so I wouldn't step on them, then it became clear
I didn't have to worry. Somehow my pace
didn't need to be altered or redirected.
No matter where they were, I missed them.
Whenever I neared, my foot would be up
in the air or land beside as if guided that way.
My dog too, trotting at my side, passed them by
every slug a lighthouse of subtle mind control
as we walked to the end of the muddy path
and back without harming a single one.

The BIRD PLANET

It's like another planet, tall trees, shade and green,
surrounded by songs of birds I cannot see

A FAMILY of DEER

Stopping for a family of deer
the mother leads the way
followed by two babies with spots
then the father with horns
who stops to glance at me
before they leave.
In just a few steps
I'm right where they were
their smell stays in the air
like the smoke of a campfire.

The UNDERWATER DOG

When she jumped
off the dock into the lake
she sunk to a yellow blur.
Underwater
it's deep and black
though she shows
standing on soft mud
eyes open
looking around.
The surface had time
to settle back into
smooth reflection
clouds and trees
before she realized
she couldn't breathe
and came back up again.

ONE MORNING INSTEAD

One morning I went in the backyard
and gathered the hippos. They were sleepy
but they followed me down the driveway
underneath the chirping branches to the
sidewalk. I know this isn't something you're
supposed to do but sometimes we do it anyway.
It was the beginning of a sunny day
and we played hippo checkers and yes
before long the traffic was stopped and
all those people who have to hurry around
had to do something else instead.

The DRAGONFLY DRIVER

He wears a bright yellow uniform
spins the big wooden wheel
and turns sharply in the wind.
For a while every day
the dragonfly shows up in the warm
sunshine above the field.
It's my lunchbreak and I like to get
out of the office for some fresh air.
I have my spot on the bench and
a field full of dandelion slopes
down to Garden Street with trees
and a view of the harbor.
Of course I like to watch that dragonfly
and I'm sure the little driver in there
knows me by now. We share
the same world and both of us
have things to do, but doing them
can wait.

not to worry

WILDLIFE REPORT

3 deer
1 bald eagle
2 ladybugs
1 swallowtail butterfly
1 spider in the bathroom

The NIGHTBIRD

Listen for
the last bird
tonight

one song

time to
turn off
the light

CLEVELAND ROAD

Lotus grow in the pond
beside the busy road
watching from the car
the air conditioner on
a white egret lands
sinking in flowers

The SAME RADIO

Open the window
the moon spins
like a record
Ohio music
crickets
a train
hurrying to
another town

FOX SUBWAY

I hoped for a chance to see the fox.
Sometimes he appears running along
the narrow, tree-lined edge between
their yard and next door.
The neighborhood is linked
by a chain of thin green paths
a fox will follow. They must learn
these routes like subways…
go right at the beechnut,
quick past the pool…
Even now, at 2 AM,
I might happen to hear
a rush of wind and see
the low orange blur go by.

ROUTE 61

From a distance they look like crows,
then something's not right, they're too big.
As the road passes the farmhouse, I can tell
three vultures are perched on their roof.
One of them shuffles next to the chimney
like a bent old man in a hot overcoat.

OHIO BUDDHA

In a garden
with hibiscus
Rose of Sharon
and birds

under the tree
eyes closed
with snails
upon his head

CROWDED MEADOW

I've been in
this dream before
like a flower
waiting for
that one bee

WATERMELON

Watching a rabbit
in the backyard
eating seeds
under the birdfeeder.
Calm as a pond
it moves on
to the garden
tasting the sweet
fallen pink flowers.
When the sprinkler
starts it slips
into the green
suitcase of leaves
and is gone.

The October bee
makes do with
dandelions

Walking the dog
a cat hiding
behind a pumpkin

A white cat
licking ice
on the porch

The YELLOW TREE

half its leaves
have flown
onto ground

they are ducks
pushed around a puddle
scattered in the wind

RABBIT NIGHTLIGHT

On the trail
all I see
a white tail

DEER POEM #2

Walking along
the museum of 7 AM
a deer painting
in the trees
watching me

DEER POEM #4

Before I got there
I was thinking I'd like
to bring a present.
What would a deer want?
I could bring an apple
but they already eat
their share off the trees.
Maybe a tangerine, or
some supermarket fruit
flown here from overseas?
One taste of that and
it would never forget.
For the rest of its life
that deer would be looking
for another pineapple.

DEER POEM #5

I told Rustle about the deer and asked,
"What do you think he's doing in their yard?"
as we passed that spot in our car.
Rustle said, "He's a spy deer.
He spies on whatever goes by."
Of course. I never considered
I'm not the only one watching
he's wearing the slouch hat and raincoat
disguised, taking notes and melting back
into the forest to report on us.
As if to lend truth to this six-year-old's theory,
I haven't seen the deer since then,
his cover is blown.

The LANGUAGE of ANIMALS

These days I'm much more interested in the language of animals. The birds at 4:30, the rabbits whispering under a parked car, a bee bumping into another one coming out of a flower.

The VOLES

I opened the file cabinet only to find the voles have been at it again. All the folders are in disarray. It will take me hours to rearrange what the voles have done. They have no regard for the alphabet or even for time itself.

The OFFICE SPIDER

A tiny spider is making a web in front of my computer screen. Of all things, its web is connected to my cup! What am I going to do? I need my tea! Careful as someone moving invisible beams, I managed to shift that spider's web and anchor it to the telephone. Unfortunately, that seemed to inspire new possibilities for expansion. It's really going gung-ho now, making that web in front of my screen, running back and forth on scaffolding. But let's face it, this office is no supermarket for spiders. How's it going to survive? So I very carefully airlifted the spider to the tree outside. A week later, I got a postcard.

The ELEPHANT in the ELEVATOR

It's very rare that I take the elevator to the second floor. It's slow and cramped and sounds like a gondola pulled by rusted chains. If someone could convince the elephant to leave, it would probably work better.

RETIRED from the CUCKOO CLOCK

I only hear one bird talking lazily from a tree somewhere behind me. He used to have a job in a cuckoo clock and it took some time before time didn't matter anymore.

The PUPPY TYPEWRITER

The minute I come in the door, the puppy jumps off the desk and runs around my feet, tapping keys and pulling at me. We play chase and tug-of-war with a piece of paper for a while before she finally settles down and takes a nap.

The OLD MOTH

She tottered into the office and told me, "I'm lost." She looked like a cocoon again, with her gray wings wrapped tightly around her. She wore big sunglasses that hid half her face. I took her outside. The morning rain left the grass steaming. I pointed to the building where she wanted to be.

The FLY TRAVEL AGENCY

Every once in a while, a fly visits the office. This isn't one of their popular tourist destinations. I can imagine the fly travel agency. Brochures and posters feature their dream vacations: a greasy diner, a roadside attraction, or a rodeo. I'm guessing our office is a hard sell. Unless their idea of excitement is circling a room a few times, looking for the way they got in.

The ZEBRA

A merry-go-round arrived in eleven boxes today. I guess it's my fault I opened one to peek inside and a zebra got out. It ran around the room in a circle, the only direction it knew, so it was pretty easy to catch and return to the box before anyone knew.

A RHINOCEROS STAMPEDE

"This is a test of the Office Alert System. In the event of a rhinoceros stampede, get close to the floor where you'll find the freshest air. Try using a phone to let responders know where you are. If the phone doesn't work, then signal from a window by waving a coat and yelling."

An HOUR with the JABBERWOCKY

He walked into the office and looked around and told me he used to work here. With a long sigh, he settled himself into a chair. He told me about the stuffed wolf in the basement, the Mother Goose paintings, and the story of the birds and other things I already forgot. Finally, he warned me: you don't want to get an old guy started talking.

The MOTH RESCUE LEAGUE

Rachel loves moths. She caught one in the studio upstairs. She held it under a glass jar on her hand and it tickled her palm. The moth was wearing socks. It left its shoes in the lining of a sweater. O, how it missed the feel of that cotton candy meadow made of wool. When she let it go outside, the moth landed on the pavement. It was raining, its feet were wet. It wondered what happened to that warm sweater it adored.

HORACE the WALRUS

Horace used to work in the employment office. He was notoriously slow and unhelpful. It was a miracle anyone got hired. After he got fired, he got another job at the Gulf gas station on Ellis Street. I found him by accident when I stopped there once. He floated behind the glass of that little booth and gave wrong directions. A year or so after that, they knocked the place out of existence and now all that's left is a plot of gravel.

PIG FARMER BLUES

He raises sixteen pigs every year, feeds them the food from his garden, stands in the middle of them and rubs their backs. It's a good feeling after a long day at the office and summer is the best time to have pigs. Next week he will let them in the turnip field. They're as happy as they will ever be.

Blue jays
busy leaving acorns
in the gutters

The rabbit bus stop
where they stand in pairs
every morning

Four deer
not the Beatles
cross the road

Looking up
to see a raven
a fat drop of rain
in my eye

A dry junco
using the leaves
for an umbrella

It passes
very slowly
the worm subway

HOUSE of MOTHS

Our first pet hung around the house upside-down on the ceilings of rooms, following us throughout day and night. Magically, it seemed to be in more than one place at a time. By and by we realized the truth, and we started counting moths. They liked to gather in the bathroom, wrap the shower curtain over their shoulders, or hang on the wall like paintings.

The CATERPILLAR KING

Sun warm on him from the tallest height of a sunflower, the Caterpillar King surveyed the realm beyond. Over the garden he saw another green land. He wanted to know what that mystery was. Others had tried crossing the road and they were lost in a sudden roaring flash. The Caterpillar King was lofty on his stalk. He couldn't wait for wings. He left the golden crown like a drop of dew while he inched back down.

The LAUGHING BUDDHA

The laughing Buddha curved the world in the steamship hold with a full load of mahogany in the hull. Some of the sailors were also taking back animals to sell in America. A monkey got loose and lived in the network of pipes that ran vines all throughout. Over the metal bolted doorway, a slip past the cook, and he could eat the food tossed up to him. A long voyage past mines and submarines, the sea turned to land. After all the cranes unloading onto train cars, the first mate drove off with a seabag and his laughing Buddha set like a wooden clock on the dashboard. For a long time, the rest of a lifetime flowed by like a wheel. At the end, in the last seconds, he finally knew. The laughing Buddha sat on the fireplace next to seashells, some photos, and a gong from the Congo.

SHE PAINTED TIGER STRIPES

She painted tiger stripes over all the swells
and curves and then she bid a cat hello
to the moon snugged against the dark
apartment bricks. Out over the tar
she danced to the steep edge of the roof
where her round bright eyes searched
the streets below. Light made lines,
people formed ants on the sandy cement,
the city sound flapped in the wind
like a blanket.

BARON of the BEES

The baron has forgotten
the game he used to play

instead of shooting biplanes
he says hello to every day

in a field all full of honey
making fleets to fill the sky

his commands they gladly carry
on the smallest wings they fly

The 500 Pound Halo

HOLY WATER

That dew
in spider circles
little water buckets
left after rain

So holy
to get close to
but I wouldn't dare
tip them
and spill
the web

PRAYING MANTIS

How many years
have children
been taunting
the praying mantis
This porky kid
says it will
jump on your neck
the other says
he wants to hit
it with a rock
but there it holds
to the window screen
of the restaurant
and here I am
telling them
please be kind
look at it
it's amazing
I feel like
the old man
in a story
from Japan
where sea turtles
turn into kings

PLAYGROUND

Find a cricket
in the grass
by the swing
tired
worn-out
from music
and moonlight
all night

TODAY

Today
a butterfly
made its way
over Lake Erie

then turned
around
again

FREE KITTENS

Another sign
a mile from one
just like it
on Berlin Road

Around here
they grow
cats like corn
then they
drawn signs
on cardboard
to give them
away

MULBERRY TREE

Canoes
parked
in shade
asleep

The tree shakes
while the flock
eats mulberries
in the leaves
above Lake Erie

Sometimes
a berry falls
and rings
on tin

BIRDS EXPECT

Birds expect
to be chased
by children

They wait
on sidewalks
or windowsills

What surprise
when suddenly
they fly

WE

We live below
a lid of clouds
bound to
the tops of trees

We follow the crows
leading the way
calling out names
in the maze

JACK'S COW

What do I know? I've never been past the fence. The field has been my home. When I say field, believe me, picture the ground packed hard like clay and here and there pockets of muddy water. That's where I used to be. Now for some reason I'm walking outside on the road. Jack is taking me somewhere.

I pretend it's okay. What do I look at? Fence posts, hedges, the clouds. I've never gone this far before. I never wonder. There's a rope around me. It doesn't hurt. Jack just pulls me along. I guess he wants me to see something.

I didn't know I could walk this far. Oh, there's a farm I never saw before. Look at that meadow. Look at the clover! I didn't know the land could grow like that. I imagine myself there…Each day in the grass tall enough to brush me. Buttercups!

Back where we live, Jack, his mother and I, we have a clapboard house sitting on dirt. I spend all day looking for something green or with petals, dreaming about a field like that…But Jack won't stop to let me in there. He pulls on my rope. We must be going somewhere very important. And Jack is so serious too, like the time he tried to fix my fence. I wish Jack would just let me look at those flowers. I guess he wants to go with this road and follow it all the way to the distant steeple and roofs of town.

If it wasn't for this rope, I'd be across that ditch in one leap. I could live in there and die of happiness.

A splash from the direction I wasn't watching made both of us jump.

Someone said something, "You selling your cow?" and Jack pulled me to a stop.

"I am," said Jack. "For a good price."

I didn't like the man who stood there leaning on a fence post all wrapped with barbed wire. I didn't like him but there was nothing I could say to Jack.

The man took a wet footstep out of the irrigation ditch. "I'll give you five magic beans," he said.

He reached in his long coat and found a flowered handkerchief. From it he poured the magic beans into his open palm.

Jack took a step closer. The shiny beans watched him like owl eyes.

I mooed. I pulled on the rope. I didn't like this at all. I know Jack. I know what's going to happen next.

A
Reversed
Cat

RICHARD'S MOUSE

His father wanted him to shoot mice. They were all around the barn, it was easy to get them, even the cats grew tired of it. After a while, so did he. Maybe he could have forgotten about them with time, letting them go like toys pushed away. He didn't though. One of them never left. It grew old with him, slowed down by age and injuries. Every day they went out walking, without a map, to travel the city streets, coming to stops, then moving on again, with that white-faced mouse whispering the way.

THE BLUE PARROT

When I was your age, my mother gave me five dollars to go to the store and buy some bread. It was a sunny day, I didn't mind, I got on my bike and jumped it off the curb, pedaling like wind. There was nobody on the street, it's a dead end, it runs out into a big wall of blackberries. I pedaled like crazy, sometimes I can make it in 109 seconds. Sometimes I slow down, take it easy so I can look at the sky while I ride.

There was a jet plane way up there spinning a web in a long white line.

At the yellow dead end sign there's a path just wide enough to ride through the vines and branches. That's my short cut to the store. Not only mine; sometimes I find the junk other people leave behind, bottles and cardboard.

The path comes out right next to the store's parking lot. I have my place to park next to the soda machine.

I could have gone past the sun on the bin of oranges and in the sliding doors, found the bread and brought it home, but there was a girl standing there holding a blue parrot.

She said, "Hi," to me and I had to stop. "Do

you want to buy this bird?" she said.

Of course I did. I gave her the five dollars and she set the bird on my shoulder.

"It won't fly away," she said.

I thanked her, she smiled, I got back on my bicycle and turned around. Out of the corner of my eye I could see the bird as I pedaled. He liked riding on my shoulder. I felt like a pirate, my bicycle was the fastest ship on the sea.

MOTH and CHILD

The night was warm with insects. In bed, he listened to the thousand songs and flutters, loving most of all the soft moth beats on his window glass. Watching the circus juggle of wings, he had an idea that took him to sleep. He dreamed of The Moth on the Moon...a moth so big it danced upon the moon. But it he could make enough light on the lawn, more than a full moon, it might fly attracted to him instead. He padded quietly through the house, past his sleeping parents, to the attic where he took Christmas lights out of a dusty box. Also, he took lamps, candles and flashlights from different silent rooms. He took all the things that could glow, piled high in his arms, through the hallway, out the door, outside. The grass was soft while he scooted around setting things up, trailing wires back inside, bringing out matches. When the lawn was lit, it was so bright it attracted moths from all over the nighttime world. Even airplanes circled, confused in the dark. He laughed at all the soaring around and waited nervously. At last, from the stars came a wind, with the biggest wings of all unspreading. His dream came true. The moth on the moon circled the lawn and swooped to the child, picked him up carefully in a cradle of legs and off they flew.

INVISIBLY FINDING the HONEY of BEES

He was led by a guide when he was a child. A friendly giraffe walked by his side, pulling on a water clear leash. Invisibly looking through the height of the clouds, the giraffe would laugh to show him the path and hide him from what to avoid. Troubles began the second he opened the door, the city could be a dangerous maze. Though it was good to know he was safe as he played, best of all were the treasures found along the way... Kites in trees, Frisbees, a boomerang from a roof, bird eggs and caterpillars and the honey of bees.

RABBIT

Free Baby Rabbits. The sign on the road arrowed him over gravel shadows, weeds clinging dust. He stopped his bicycle in front of the barn. He leaned it angled on its kickstand and left it in the sun to go knock upon the door.

"Hello?" he asked the quiet...Quiet, but not utterly silent. He could hear the peeping swallows as they jigsawed overhead. Poplars rustled their green overcoats by the river. "Hello?"

"Yes! Hello!" said a woman. She clattered at the latches and he helped her open the door.

He smiled as the light of day showed her up, for she wore on her head a tall striped hat that Dr. Seuss could have drawn. She smiled too, her very old face making spider webs. "You came for a rabbit?"

"Yes, that's right. I have a basket with a blanket," he pointed back towards his bicycle, "to take the rabbit home."

So she looked into him with wide eyes that he felt go inside, that felt around his heart and searched his mind. "Good," she decided when she was done. "I'll give you one."

From her patched dress, she pulled a rabbit out

of a pocket. "This is yours now." She let his arms go around the fur.

He was spellbound, holding stars. He cradled the rabbit back to the bicycle. He unleafed the quilt in the basket over the tire where the world would be covered until they got home.

Then as he rode away, turning around to wave, she took off her hat to listen with her tall, revealed long rabbit ears and she wished them a safe departing.

WORM SALVAGE WORK

Spring rain
brings them
above ground

Stranding them
on tar

There's only so much
you can do

Saving a worm
is taking a meal
from a bird

The HUMMING BIRDS

The birds
have forgotten
their words
now only
tunes remain
they sit on
branches and hum

SILKWORMS

Suspended
from trees
just beginning
to blossom

At 2 AM

A goose
goes over
the house
waking me
with a horn

The PACKARD HATCHERY

Now I've gone to great pains
to reverse the tide of history.
There's no reason to believe
that once again we can't see
thousands of Packards
on the roads of America.
What I began is a hatchery.
There are three cement pools
where they start out,
little fingerlings,
flickers of silver chrome
Packards no more than
a few inches long.
They school together
and drive in endless circles.
I care for them, make sure
they grow strong.
Of course it's a slow process
but eventually they will be released.
It's breathtaking to see it happen,
when the waters of the last big tank
shimmer and out drives a new herd.
The Packards move cautiously at first
then picking up speed and really
making a run for it when their wheels
get the feel of the sunlit tar.

DIRECTIONS FOLDED to a BIRD'S WING

Walk down the steep hill, on a sidewalk split by the roots of trees arching overhead. Turn the corner to the left and then you can hear the birds. It's an aviary attached to a house like a screened porch that's trying to bring the sky down and cage it in a space only ten-by-ten feet. I've seen this through all the seasons. In the gray wet Seattle winter it's covered by plastic so the cold can't get in. Rather than that, I'll remember it as summer when those African finches are singing their hearts out and the sparrows and even the crows will come to the bent wire corners to listen.

A BROOM

A crow
carrying
one stick
to sweep
the tree

A CRANEFLY

A cranefly
in this clearing
carrying sunlight
on its wings

BIRD TAXI

At 4 AM I heard the birds at the end of the street. Almost an hour later, a robin started in our yard, then I heard a car motor arrive and stop at the curb. I was too tired to get up and look out the window, so I let myself see it another way. I pictured the yellow shiny door of a checkered cab open. With the sound of pouring water, all those birdsfrom down the street flew out and found places in our tree. A new day was beginning, they were making the rounds, singing their hearts out. So thick you could walk on the sound, or float on it, let your mattress drift like a raft if it wasn't 6 o'clock and time to get up.

OCTOPUS *MOTORS*

introduction

ANIMALS in EVERYTHING

I didn't know this was going to turn into a book. It began with reading Richard Hugo in Wilson Library, while I was busy writing a novel, then these stories started appearing. I realized there are animals in everything. They arrived on their own and they walked themselves onto an ark I didn't know I was building.

—July 2023, A.F

300 MOONS LATER

I remember going to The Richard Hugo House on Capitol Hill. Up the steps, in the big door, it really was a house, with carpeting and easy chairs and a bulletin board. I was looking for directions on how to be a writer. As if that could be put onto a notecard, posted with the contests and workshops and a lost pet. Now, 300 moons later, I finally got around to reading *The Triggering Town*. These are the pages that should have been the shingles nailed all over that big rain-colored house in Seattle.

CUSTODIAL SERVICES

In my dream last night, I fell asleep at a crowded lecture about mountain climbing in the Himalayas. Still within the dream, I woke in a dark, empty auditorium—no not quite empty, a custodian was pushing a cart into the room. I apologized and flustered. It's interesting to know there are custodians behind the scenes in dreams. I know over the years I've created plenty of havoc for them with gorillas and great white sharks, crashing planes, floods, wars, and other mayhem. Fortunately, they're ready every night for more.

The FIVE-SECOND GIRAFFE

Snow falls outside the window, soft and steady, big as radio dials. I've been doing nothing this morning, just watching the way snow covers the roof next door like the voice of Nat King Cole. The world is under a spell, I can tell. For the next five seconds a giraffe stood in the driveway. It was more prepared for the moment than me. It was wearing a scarf.

UNICORN DELIVERY SERVICE

Ashtabula is beautiful this time of year, but this isn't Ashtabula. It's cold, raining off and on, windy and gray, the day before Halloween. My daughter has turned into a unicorn, she couldn't wait for tomorrow. She'll be that way for breakfast, and wear a crown onto the school bus, on her way to being a unicorn all day.

MOUSE FACT

During its life, a mouse doesn't move more than a hundred feet from where it's born. Actually, I can't guarantee that's true. When she told me that at work today, I believed her. It was only later that I wondered how that was tested. Did they have an airplane hangar, did they make a circle a hundred feet wide and put a baby mouse in the middle? Did the years pass slowly in that pen, fluorescent lights overhead, while it wandered back and forth, never venturing beyond the imaginary limits? Who knows. It's easier just to believe.

300 FEET

But then I thought about another mouse. This one was young and had dreams. She was no ordinary mouse. She took a bus, actually it was a turtle, and she watched the familiar world crawl from sight, past the border all the way to the edge of 24th Street. That's where she stepped off the turtle into weeds as tall as trees, three hundred feet from home.

SPRING DOG

She stands outside on the path, staring at the street, knowing something is happening. Birds are singing. The air is wearing less cold. She is waiting for a parade she knows is on the way.

The DIARY of a DOLLAR STORE ARBORIST

This winter we had a windstorm that damaged a tree, I tried to prop a branch with an old broken chair. That didn't work. Our dog watched my latest project. Then I went to the Dollar Store and got some bungee cords to make a sling for the branch. That did the trick, this week, it burst with cherry blossoms, leaning in the backyard like a pirate courting with flowers.

The ANT PEDDLER

He knocked on the door and our dog barked. I opened the door and there he stood, wearing a strange uniform like a rocket pilot. He told me he just happened to be in the neighborhood and he wanted to know if we had ants. This is the season to welcome them, he said. He tried his best to convince me to open the crawlspace vents and let them in. "Put sugar on your kitchen counter and they'll build roads and farms and little towns, and you'll grow to love their company," he promised as I shut the door.

OCTOPUS MOTORS

This one doesn't seem inclined today. It spent all morning in the corner, wrapped up like a flower. If it doesn't move in an hour, I'll call a mechanic. If that doesn't work, I'll get a florist.

The LURCHER

The lurcher is an English breed of dog, sleek, not unlike a whippet or a greyhound. On Sunday I saw one loping up the sidewalk. It was chased by a cowboy. For all his skills, it wouldn't come to him. When his wife appeared, the dog ran straight to her. The cowboy walked slowly after them.

HEMINGWAY'S MOSQUITO

The girl in the office is afraid of a mosquito. Every time it comes near her, she leaps from the desk and backs around the office in terror. I felt just shy of bragging when I offered to help. I said mosquitos don't scare me. I've bagged hundreds in my time. I sounded like Hemingway rowing to shore with a skeleton. For a second I had it in my sights, a perfect kill, then I stumbled on the telephone cord and lost it against the field-colored twill of the carpet.

The SHIP of MONSTERS

He's told the story before about how he had to defend the Earth only this time it's true. A rocket lands near his ranch. A vampire is after him with her outer space crew. He prefers her sister and he sings to her from his horse. He's a fool but he's fearless. All he needs to do is capture their command belt. He fights a giant spider and gets trapped inside a tree and she hears him. They leave this planet in her rocket. He's up there in the night sky now, on that little green dot of light, Venus.

The OFFICE PEST

I had to call Facilities Management and they sent someone over with a big butterfly net and they caught the office pest. What a relief. The room has returned to a sort of calm. All I hear is the gentle purr of the ceiling fan.

BALANCE

A junco on roller-skates swerves around me, scratching into the dust, its little wheels turn and chirp beneath the leaves before it stops. It flaps its wings like someone catching their balance.

CHICKEN INTRODUCTION

These are the chickens I walk by every morning on my way to work. There are three of them. One is checkered black and white. The other two are brown, I think. I always say hi. They're too busy to reply. Tomorrow will be the same. You now know as much about them as I do.

PALMS

When I travel, send me to The Bob Hope Airport in Burbank. You get to walk outside onto the plane like Humphrey Bogart. It's always sunny, you can breathe the flowers churned up by jet motors and Ingrid Bergman has got your rabbit soul in her palms.

A FLY in the SUNSHINE

It's enjoying the warm June weather. We've gone a long gray winter and a rainy spring. Six pairs of boots are set beside it and a miniature windbreaker on a rack. I don't want to disturb its spot on the door handle. I feel the same way. I'm in no rush to go back to work.

RABBIT CARPET

I want to forgive the cat next door for killing the rabbit and leaving its body dried flat behind a tree and I want to think there's a better world that rabbit went to where things like this don't happen.

The GIANT MOTH

Its wings are the color of concrete, spread across the entire city. Run through with roads and a highway, apartments and parking lots. Only from the air can you tell the shape outlined against the forested hills and the bay. We're all living on a giant moth and we have no idea when it will fly away.

The SNAKE HOLIDAY

We know he's there. He lives somewhere around our house, in a foundation crack, or wormed under the cement step, or hiding under a warm rock. It's a rare day when you get to see him. On a calendar it would be made a holiday right before the Fourth of July.

MINARET

In the early dawn, I don't know what time it was, I didn't look at the clock, it was dark in our bedroom, and each time the train sounded its horn, a coyote would cry out in pain. There was a minaret made of night and the prayer was repeated as the train rolled on the tracks through our town.

The LOST PARROT REWARD

There's a parrot lost in the woods. You can't miss the poster with the big word: REWARD. I've been looking for it. In the woods I heard thrush and blue jay, wrens and robins and ravens. I read International Birdwatcher every day. No parrot in the canopy calls, no pirate talk squawked at me. Don't think this will be one of those stories with a fairytale ending.

The 20-MINUTE PARKING SIGN

Today it's in the center of swallows and dragonflies. They all orbit around it like a circus ride. If a car arrives it will have to duck.

The AIR TODAY

The World Health Federation finds the air today VERY UNHEALTHY. There are fires on the Cascades, up into Canada, and the sun is science-fiction red. I walked home wearing a mask. Once upon a time there were dinosaurs. They were here in this very spot. Think of lizards flying through volcano skies, then notice the tiny blue aphids in the driveway floating in the ash like fairies.

A-1 CROW SERVICE

They always park on the side of the road in a dusty car. They hold wings before the dashboard. They could be saying a prayer, it's hard to tell, the windshield is rough as an agate and to be honest I've never made eye contact with them, not even a wave, while I walk by in the mornings with somewhere oh-so important to be.

BEATRIX

So far today I've seen nearly ten rabbits. Three of them were in our driveway. One of them is an old friend. I've been watching it for a long time, I don't know how long they live, it just appears every morning in the dandelions. Lately it's been wearing Peter Rabbit's torn blue coat, chewing the cigarette Farmer McGregor dropped in a cabbage row.

RABBIT ROUTINE

The rabbits have their routes across backyards, starting with the blackberry hedge by the woods, to the cedar fence around the house and all stations in between and back again. This is their neighborhood routine, how they circulate is unknowable unless you live in a trolley.

24th STREET TROUT

One evening I was walking home from work on 24th and a guy was grilling fish outside his garage. He turned when he heard my feet on the gravel and he asked me, "You want some trout?"

COTTONWOOD LEAVES

I stop on the path to watch a rabbit fishing the stream. He makes lures out of silver cottonwood leaves, binds them to the line of a bamboo pole and casts. The current never stops flowing from the mountain. He doesn't catch anything but the branches overhead and snags underwater. The lures are left hooked, sparkling down there like treasures, and caught in the trees like tinsel.

PET STORE MEMORIAL

It's been years since the pet store burned to the ground. There's no sign of the animals who used to live there. Nothing left but rubble. I saw a pigeon and asked if it takes a lot of courage to face something so tragic and watch the land become a shadow. The pigeon told me it was new here and didn't know.

MISSING INGREDIENTS

Zucchini, potatoes, broccoli, a pepper, mushrooms, peas, coconut milk and two ingredients that I forgot to add to the curry tonight. They're still in the fridge. I imagine this happening in a kitchen underground when a rabbit wife set her fork down and knew but didn't ask her husband about the missing carrots and asparagus.

A MOMENT in the SPOTLIGHT

This is the first time I've seen anyone play a cow like a piano.

47

The giant squid sat at the department of motor vehicles. Its number was stuck to a sucker while it waited in a plastic seat. "Eighty two," the speaker crackled. The squid's big eye glanced at the paper it held...47...

TWO NURSES

They're either from the hospice or the assisted living center. The first one surprised us, you don't often see people wearing uniforms on the path. She avoided eye contact and went by solemn and silent as taxidermy. Whatever she was thinking made a cloud around her. A minute further, another nurse walked past. They were both wearing tags like birds with the name of where they were from, where they saw death come and go.

The MOTORCYCLE COP

I didn't even hear the purr of the motorcycle as it crept up the path behind me and stopped. He said he was looking for someone and he described them. I was glad it wasn't me. He used to ride down Holly Street and weave in and out like a wolf. One time he parked at the bagel shop and the big Harley fell on top of him and pinned him to the ground. There was no rush to help him.

The SLY OLD FOX

One of D's peculiar traits was leaving two-gallon milk jugs on the library shelves. They were filled with tap water, emergency stashes in case of disaster. He was ready for it. When the dust settled, he just had to reach a shaking seventy-year-old hand up to the top shelf.

The ORANGE DOT

We drove past her apartment and looked for her window and there it was. For an instant. There was no way of knowing that was a goldfish floating across the glass. It was only a tiny orange dot. There was no way of knowing the kitchen faucet was left on and the room was filled with water and anyone opening the door would let out a lake.

The CHAMELEON

I expected Dorothy to be the way I remembered her, in a checkered dress, a blue ribbon in her hair, singing, holding a basket with Toto. Can she still fly in twisters, can she still chameleon from black and white to color and back? What about her friends, the scarecrow, the lion, and the tin man? When I saw her again along the waterline at Poe's Point, she was talking to a mermaid.

AMERICAN NEIGHBORHOODS on the MOON

I was doing time in a prison on the moon. Everyone's heard stories about it. You've seen the movies. I knew I wouldn't do well there. I had to escape somehow, dig a mole tunnel with a wooden spoon, pop out a hundred yards past the electric fence. I could run from crater to crater until I got to the Sea of Tranquility.

The ALLIGATOR

He crawls around in the tunnels too. He cuts through the fences and backlots and drops out of sight in culverts where the water pools. An echo or splash from him sounds like an alligator.

ON the WAY to SOME FLOWERS

The back of the truck is stacked tall with a mountain of scrap metal and junk. It's been parked here a while. I think maybe the motor died on the hill like a snail that ran out of steam on the way to some flowers. Two people are curled deep inside there on a hot afternoon, living in a shell with the pearl worn to rust.

A BIRD with SMALL POCKETS

When I opened the door, a hummingbird flew into the house. I turned in slow-motion, only catching the scratch it made in the air on its way to the kitchen. I took a step. It shot past me again, out the door into the daylight. I don't know what it got from the kitchen, a drop of sliced watermelon or the dew on a bottlecap, whatever it needed would be infinitesimal.

SEA ANEMONES

If I think of the Prairie Market, I remember the barges we rode down the aisles between all the cans and bags and cereal boxes and when we got there, whoever was steering us would have to gather speed past the candy while we reached out like sea anemones.

THURSDAY MORNING

The street sweeper takes its elephant time past our house. It makes a loud gray furrow in the window. For about a minute it mooches along until it fades into the rest of the Thursday morning sounds.

FLYING CONDITIONS

It was eighty-one degrees last night. We have fans going on every floor. A breeze runs through our house like a stream. When I opened the door this morning to let the dog outside, we almost fell. The house was hovering in the air, caught by the corner, held tangled up in the telephone wires. And what a racket—we're roaring over the cement foundation loud as a zeppelin.

SYLVIA

She preferred the company of children. Sooner or later she would find an excuse to take her from the kitchen table cigarette cloud and she would slip to the porch. That's where the kids were playing. The sun in the pines, blue jays, a view of the tide making progress across the flats. She played their games and laughed and they always gave her a hug when it was time to go home.

OUR DOG'S FRIEND is LEAVING

Both her cars won't start so she drives a school bus. That's hers—the Chevrolet Blue Bird parked at the curb. She quit her job here, she accepted a better one in California. She is leaving tonight in that bus, but she had to say goodbye to our dog. There's more to her story, this is the only part I see.

PANGOLIN TAKE-OUT

It was amazing the way the whole town turned up to help me find the pangolin. It affirmed my belief in the kindness of the town and these people. We didn't find the pangolin though—you would have thought we could—but I expect we'll run across it at some point. It's not that big a town.

This MUCH WATER

For Clyde

The next time I see the Ganges, it won't be like today. The red morning sun will paddle on the river like a bird. I'll be in a whole other life. Each one is another dream. The last time I saw this much water feels like yesterday.

The STAFFORD HOTEL LODGING HOUSE

Gene Vincent is on the radio. Someone is parking their DeSoto. The backseat has a suitcase and some cardboard boxes and a tilted parakeet cage. The car makes a lot of noise fitting into the spot next to the curb. 702 ½ West Holly. Someone leans in the windshield, reading the Room to Let sign.

OLYMPIA

They were so in love. He would call her from Olympia and hear her voice and that's all it took. He would say, "I'm on the way," and it was true, he would jump on the very next Greyhound bus.

The WORLD'S HEAVYWEIGHT CHAMPION BOXING KANGAROO

Is he immune to all the world's challenges? Has he been seen in a limousine transported like royalty? Does he stare at the wall at night, muddied by the dull ringing in his head, counting the times he's been hit instead of counting sheep?

The FOIBLES of FEINSTEIN

He put all his foibles in a wheelbarrow. Whatever they were doesn't matter anymore. They were tipping and spilling, some fell out on the bumpy way to the cliff. He had to wait for a pelican cabby from Brooklyn and he had to pay upfront for the weight to be unloaded and flown offshore where a whale knew the way to a whirlpool.

The KNOW-IT-ALL

I cross the street all the time. It's not dangerous if you know what you're doing. Relax, I know all about cars and trucks and buses and bicycles. I'm not a kitten anymore, I've been around for years. My advice is, if you really want to get to the other side, you just have to run like hell.

STILL

The rustling stopped, the tall stalks settled. Nothing left a trail in the grass, there's not much to track. Surrounded by the sound of the field, whatever it was quietly joined the flowers. It's good at being still, but we'll see who moves first. If it was a tree, it would be an apple, if it was an apple, it would be an apple with a worm in it.

The CLOVER LOS ANGELES

In a clover city the bees taxi back and forth on routes that hover just above the grass, stopping at each flower top where the fare is measured in ingredients for making honey.

The BALLERINAS

She left the porchlight on so she could watch the moths come in from the dark and bounce around it.

TUESDAY AFTERNOON

A butterfly grows tired of chasing her.

The TURTLE on MYRTLE

For hundreds of years people have been renting rooms like the ones in the house on Myrtle Street. It sits on the corner and stares at the traffic and clouds. The green roof has three chimneys on the shell and a TV antenna that still gets Channel 12. The sea moves slowly further ashore, digging in claws with each wave.

ARBUCKLE'S DOG

I know that world of theirs, I've been there in dreams where our gravity doesn't apply and I can fly between the tenement buildings. You have a brown and white dog named Luke who moves twice as fast as us, outracing cars, climbing ladders, diving off piers like a fishing lure. Arbuckle's dog never slows down until the end of day when he lands on a pillow and his legs keep running in his sleep.

The RED DOT

There's a sale on red riding hoods and she bought a little one for her friend. No bigger than a sunflower seed, the coat was just right to avoid wolf detection. With the hood pulled up, there was no ladybug to be seen. It rolled in her hand like a berry. She stopped at the edge of the woods and listened. On her palm was a little red dot that could hide on a leaf or dwindle to nothing if it wanted to.

WEDNESDAY MORNING

Two people in blue shirts are restocking the vending machine, talking about *The Lord of the Rings*. Yesterday, the janitor was vacuuming to Frank Sinatra. These are the people I see at this hour. Tomorrow might be a circus horse.

A BIRTHDAY CANDLE FACTORY

The assembly line is a river of candles waiting for breath and a wish. At the top of the hour, they stop all the machinery and they're raising their gloves to the ceiling and soon everyone begins to sing. Even when they go back to work and all you hear are machines their song doesn't leave the air, it's circling the world all the time like a long-distance whimbrel.

CATERPILLAR INSTRUCTIONS

In the morning be thankful to wake on a leaf. If it's raining be a part of the rain. If there's sunshine be glad that you're warm. In your thoughts, carefully unfold your new and improved butterfly directions.

TIDE

She wrote you a letter delivered by seahorse. You stood in a tidepool to read it. Water connects you. You look around for something to write on. You answer her on an oyster shell with a pearl rolling round inside.

MONTGOMERY STREET

It's hot today, we agree on that. I ask him where the cat is and he tells me, "He's outside, under a car."

The NEIGHBORHOOD LION

The lawns are burned by the sun, turned golden brown. The neighborhood lion goes from yard to yard, laying down and fading in with the ground. The orange daylily next door sways when the lion wags its tail.

A HUNDRED SWORDFISH

Everyone wanted a swordfish shadow. You might see a hundred a day. They were sold in stores and fairgrounds, and counterfeits were made in sweatshops offshore. There's always a need for more. A shadow can only last so long before it sizzles on the hot tar.

MONDAY MORNING

Like me, the spider making tracks across the floor has somewhere to be. I don't ask if it's late to work or on some errand or what, but I disrupted its plan when I caught it and let it free outside. A familiar song is playing, we all know this time of day, when we find ourselves lifted out of a web we were stuck in and carried to a place like the early morning backyard.

The CHICKEN

After a hard summer rain, the field shines diamonds and I found a pair of eagle wings left drying on a branch. I don't know if you're expecting me to put them on and start flying. This isn't that kind of story. I left them where they were. I'm not taking chances.

A HOUSE on FOREST STREET

A jellyfish chandelier haunts a window on Forest Street. I know if I was standing on that stairwell, the house would be silent except for the tentacles crackling like a campfire, slowly turning, as the jellyfish catches the sun and glows like the moon.

FISH

There are plenty of ghosts in Seattle, a whole city of them, and it's no surprise The Richard Hugo House is one of them. It's migrated from the address on East Olive Street, it's free to move unanchored. Poetry keeps drifting and swimming around the city. Nets float from it, brushing the tops of hedges, fences, cars, as fishing lines trawl the cement. I can still put myself in there, pushing out the wooden door with my hand roped around a fish.

OCTOPUS MOTORS
Written in Spring and Summer 2023

the
new book of
endangered
birds

ANIMAL INDEX:

Alligators:
255
Ants:
101, 239
Aphids:
247
Bats:
102
Bears:
26
Bees:
94, 130, 141, 149, 150, 164-165, 174, 188, 190, 194, 205, 263
Birds:
15, 16, 54, 56-57, 62, 64, 69, 74, 86, 89, 90, 94, 95, 98, 103, 108, 109-111, 112, 115, 116, 118, 119, 128, 133, 134, 137, 139, 147, 148, 149, 150, 152-158, 159-162, 174, 179, 185, 186, 187, 196, 201, 211, 212, 213, 218-219, 224, 225, 227, 228, 229, 242, 246, 247, 252, 256, 258, 259, 260, 266, 270
Butterflies:
15, 82, 124, 149, 209, 241, 264
Capybaras:
96

Caterpillars:

61, 202, 267

Cats:

32-33, 42-43, 85, 87, 99, 107, 121, 125, 149, 165, 175, 190, 210, 262, 268

Chameleon:

254

Cows:

55, 71, 104, 106, 135, 144, 176, 214-215, 251

Coyotes:

75, 103, 245

Craneflies:

228

Crickets:

186, 209

Deer:

91, 92, 98, 105, 113, 178, 180, 192-193, 201

Dinosaurs:

247

Dogs:

18, 19, 24, 29, 30-31, 40-41, 84, 88, 122, 129, 179, 181, 190, 196, 238, 240, 257, 258, 260, 265

Dragonflies:

85, 183, 246

Ducks:

34-35, 99, 191

Elephants:

69, 195, 257

Fireflies:
81
Fish:
38, 60, 87, 120, 226, 249, 253, 269, 271
Flies:
114, 140, 197, 243
Foxes:
187, 253
Frogs:
61, 78, 138
Giraffes:
159-162, 221, 236
Goats:
70
Gorillas:
117, 118, 127
Grasshoppers:
59
Hippos:
182
Horses:
16, 82, 88, 166-172, 241, 266
Jabberwocky:
199
Jellyfish:
270
Kangaroos:
261

Lions:
45, 47, 268
Mermaids:
141, 163
Mice:
66, 217, 237
Moles:
177, 254
Monkeys:
93, 142, 203
Mosquitos:
240
Moths:
24, 58, 131, 135, 197, 199, 202, 220, 244, 263
Ocelots:
73
Octopus:
19, 239
Ostrich:
51
Owls:
80, 90
Pangolins:
259
Pets:
18, 39, 46, 234
Pigeons:
250

Pigs:
200
Praying Mantis:
208
Rabbits:
17, 25, 52, 72, 92, 97, 102, 111, 123, 175, 178, 189, 201, 222-223, 243, 244, 248, 249, 250
Rhinoceros:
198
Sea Anemones:
256
Seahorses:
81, 267
Seals:
22-23, 36-37
Sharks:
235
Sheep:
136
Silkworms:
225
Snails:
79, 93, 188, 255
Snakes:
49, 245
Spiders:
71, 185, 195, 207, 269

Squid:
251
Starfish:
65
Tigers:
83, 86, 204
Toads:
66-67, 68
Turtles:
264
Unicorns:
84, 236
Voles:
194
Walrus:
91, 200
Weasels:
76
Whales:
83, 105, 145, 261
Wingtripples:
50
Wolves:
28, 252, 265
Worms:
44, 201, 224, 262
Zebras:
198

Picture from *The Wires and Circuits of Earth* (2022)

Books by Good Deed Rain

Saint Lemonade, Allen Frost, 2014. Two novels illustrated by the author in the manner of the old Big Little Books.

Playground, Allen Frost, 2014. Poems collected from seven years of chapbooks.

Roosevelt, Allen Frost, 2015. A Pacific Northwest novel set in July, 1942, when a boy and a girl search for a missing elephant. Illustrated throughout by Fred Sodt.

5 Novels, Allen Frost, 2015. Novels written over five years, featuring circus giants, clockwork animals, detectives and time travelers.

The Sylvan Moore Show, Allen Frost, 2015. A short story omnibus of 193 stories written over 30 years.

Town in a Cloud, Allen Frost, 2015. A three part book of poetry, written during the Bellingham rainy seasons of fall, winter, and spring.

A Flutter of Birds Passing Through Heaven: A Tribute to Robert Sund, 2016. Edited by Allen Frost and Paul Piper. The story of a legendary Ish River poet & artist.

At the Edge of America, Allen Frost, 2016. Two novels in one book blend time travel in a mythical poetic America.

Lake Erie Submarine, Allen Frost, 2016. A two week vacation in Ohio inspired these poems, illustrated by the author.

and Light, Paul Piper, 2016. Poetry written over three years. Illustrated with watercolors by Penny Piper.

The Book of Ticks, Allen Frost, 2017. A giant collection of 8 mysterious adventures featuring Phil Ticks. Illustrated throughout by Aaron Gunderson.

I Can Only Imagine, Allen Frost, 2017. Five adventures of love and heartbreak dreamed in an imaginary world. Cover & color illustrations by Annabelle Barrett.

The Orphanage of Abandoned Teenagers, Allen Frost, 2017. A fictional guide for teens and their parents. Illustrated by the author.

In the Valley of Mystic Light: An Oral History of the Skagit Valley Arts Scene, 2017. A comprehensive illustrated tribute. Edited by Claire Swedberg & Rita Hupy.

Different Planet, Allen Frost, 2017. Four science fiction adventures: reincarnation, robots, talking animals, outer space and clones. Cover & illustrations by Laura Vasyutynska.

Go with the Flow: A Tribute to Clyde Sanborn, 2018. Edited by Allen Frost. The life and art of a timeless river poet. In beautiful living color!

Homeless Sutra, Allen Frost, 2018. Four stories: Sylvan Moore, a flying monk, a water salesman, and a guardian rabbit.

The Lake Walker, Allen Frost 2018. A little novel set in black and white like one of those old European movies about death and life.

A Hundred Dreams Ago, Allen Frost, 2018. A winter book of poetry and prose. Illustrated by Aaron Gunderson.

Almost Animals, Allen Frost, 2018. A collection of linked stories, thinking about what makes us animals.

The Robotic Age, Allen Frost, 2018. A vaudeville magician and his faithful robot track down ghosts. Illustrated throughout by Aaron Gunderson.

Kennedy, Allen Frost, 2018. This sequel to *Roosevelt* is a coming-of-age fable set during two weeks in 1962 in a mythical Kennedyland. Illustrated throughout by Fred Sodt.

Fable, Allen Frost, 2018. There's something going on in this country and I can best relate it in fable: the parable of the rabbits, a bedtime story, and the diary of our trip to Ohio.

Elbows & Knees: Essays & Plays, Allen Frost, 2018. A thrilling collection of writing about some of my favorite subjects, from B-movies to Brautigan.

The Last Paper Stars, Allen Frost 2019. A trip back in time to the 20 year old mind of Frankenstein, and two other worlds of the future.

Walt Amherst is Awake, Allen Frost, 2019. The dreamlife of an office worker. Illustrated throughout by Aaron Gunderson.

When You Smile You Let in Light, Allen Frost, 2019. An atomic love story written by a 23 year old.

Pinocchio in America, Allen Frost, 2019. After 82 years buried underground, Pinocchio returns to life behind a car repair shop in America.

Taking Her Sides on Immortality, Robert Huff, 2019. The long awaited poetry collection from a local, nationally renowned master of words.

Florida, Allen Frost, 2019. Three days in Florida turned into a book of sunshine inspired stories.

Blue Anthem Wailing, Allen Frost, 2019. My first novel written in college is an apocalyptic, Old Testament race through American shadows while Amelia Earhart flies overhead.

The Welfare Office, Allen Frost, 2019. The animals go in and out of the office, leaving these stories as footprints.

Island Air, Allen Frost, 2019. A detective novel featuring haiku, a lost library book and streetsongs.

Imaginary Someone, Allen Frost, 2020. A fictional memoir featuring 45 years of inspirations and obstacles in the life of a writer.

Violet of the Silent Movies, Allen Frost, 2020. A collection of starry-eyed short story poems, illustrated by the author.

The Tin Can Telephone, Allen Frost, 2020. A childhood memory novel set in 1975 Seattle, illustrated by author like a coloring book.

Heaven Crayon, Allen Frost, 2020. How the author's first book *Ohio Trio* would look if printed as a Big Little Book. Illustrated by the author.

Old Salt, Allen Frost, 2020. Authors of a fake novel get chased by tigers. Illustrations by the author.

A Field of Cabbages, Allen Frost, 2020. The sequel to *The Robotic Age* finds our heroes in a race against time to save Sunny Jim's ghost. Illustrated by Aaron Gunderson.

River Road, Allen Frost, 2020. A paperboy delivers the news to a ghost town. Illustrated by the author.

The Puttering Marvel, Allen Frost, 2021. Eleven short stories with illustrations by the author.

Something Bright, Allen Frost, 2021. 106 short story poems walking with you from winter into spring. Illustrated by the author.

The Trillium Witch, Allen Frost, 2021. A detective novel about witches in the Pacific Northwest rain. Illustrated by the author.

Cosmonaut, Allen Frost, 2021. Yuri Gagarin stars in this novel that follows his rocket landing in an American town. Midnight jazz, folk music, mystery and sorcery. Illustrated by the author.

Thriftstore Madonna, Allen Frost, 2021. 124 summer story poems. Illustrated by the author.

Half a Giraffe, Allen Frost, 2021. A magical novel about a counterfeiter and his unusual, beloved pet. Illustrated by the author.

Lexington Brown & The Pond Projector, Allen Frost, 2022. An underwater invention takes three friends through time. Illustrated by Aaron Gunderson.

The Robert Huck Museum, Allen Frost, 2022. The artist's life story told in photographs, woodcuts, paintings, prints and drawings.

Mrs. Magnusson & Friends, Allen Frost, 2022. A collection of 13 stories featuring mystery and magic and ginkgo leaves.

Magic Island, Allen Frost, 2022. There's a memory machine in this magic novel that takes us to college.

A Red Leaf Boat, Allen Frost, 2022. Inspired by Japan, this book of 142 poems is the result of walking in autumn.

Forest & Field, Allen Frost, 2022. 117 forest and field recordings made during the summer months, ending with a lullaby.

The Wires and Circuits of Earth, Allen Frost, 2022. 11 stories from a train station pulp magazine.

The Air Over Paris, Allen Frost, 2023. This novel reveals the truth about semi-sentient speedbumps from Mars.

Neptunalia, Allen Frost, 2023. A movie-novel for Neptune, featuring mystery in a Counterfeit Reality machine. Illustrated by Aaron Gunderson.

The Worrys, Allen Frost, 2023. A family of weasels look for a better life and get it. Illustrated by Tai Vugia.

American Mantra, Allen Frost, 2023. The future needs poetry to sleep at night. Only one man and one woman can save the world. Illustrated by Robert Huck.

One Drop in the Milky Way, Allen Frost, 2023. A novel about retiring, with a little help from a skeleton and Abraham Lincoln.

Follow Your Friend, Allen Frost, 2023. A collection of animals from sewn, stapled, and printed books spanning 34 years of writing.

Books by Bottom Dog Press

Ohio Trio, Allen Frost, 2001. Three short novels written in magic fields and small towns of Ohio. Reprinted as *Heaven Crayon* in 2020.

Bowl of Water, Allen Frost, 2004. Poetry. From the glass factory to when you wake up.

Another Life, Allen Frost, 2007. Poetry. From the last Ohio morning to the early bird.

Home Recordings, Allen Frost, 2009. Poetry. Dream machinery, filming Caruso, benign time travel.

The Mermaid Translation, Allen Frost, 2010. A bathysphere novel with Philip Marlowe.

Selected Correspondence of Kenneth Patchen, Edited by Larry Smith and Allen Frost, 2012. Amazing artist letters.

The Wonderful Stupid Man, Allen Frost, 2012. Short stories go from Aristotle's first car to the 500 dollar fool.

BIRDCOAT

When you need air
to get up and away
from crooked ground
and all that's wrong
try on the birdcoat

Its colored feathers
are woven in yarns
its wings are arms

The roofs like bottlecaps below
while crows and even clouds
will swim out of your path

Milton Keynes UK
Ingram Content Group UK Ltd.
UKHW010117011223
433552UK00004B/270